The
Missouri
Review

Volume XVIII Number 3   1995

University of Missouri-Columbia

EDITOR

Speer Morgan

MANAGING EDITOR

Greg Michalson

ASSOCIATE EDITORS

William Peden, Jo Sapp, Evelyn Somers

OFFICE MANAGER

Dedra Earl

SENIOR ADVISORS

Mary Creger, Jeff Galbraith, Kristen Harmon,
Pamela McClure, Kris Somerville, Jeff Thomson

ADVISORS

Tracy Benbrook, Karl Foelsche, Reeves Hamilton,
Jennifer Jones, Diedre Kindsfather, Stephanie Komen,
Hoa Ngo, Kirstin Rogers, Kylie Shafferkoetter, Melissa Wright

INTERNS

Seth Bro, Ed Fogarty, Joel Huggins,
Julie Laune, Sarah Oster, David Schlansker

The Missouri Review is published by the College of Arts & Science of the University of Missouri-Columbia, with private contributions and assistance from the Missouri Arts Council and the National Endowment for the Arts.

"Colonel Sellers" by Mark Twain: previously unpublished material copyrighted 1995 by Richard A. Watson and Chemical Bank, as trustees of the Mark Twain Foundation, used by permission.

Cartoons in this issue by Carole Cable.

The editors invite submissions of poetry, fiction, and essays of a general literary interest with a distinctly contemporary orientation. Manuscripts will not be returned unless accompanied by a stamped, self-addressed envelope. Please address all correspondence to The Editors, *The Missouri Review*, 1507 Hillcrest Hall, University of Missouri, Columbia, Missouri 65211.

SUBSCRIPTIONS

1 year (3 issues), $19.00
2 years (6 issues), $35.00
3 years (9 issues), $45.00

Copyright © 1995 by The Curators of the University of Missouri
ISSN 0191 1961   **ISBN** 1-879758-15-6
Typesetting by HiTec Typeset   Printed by Thomson-Shore
Distributed by: Ingram Periodicals and B. DeBoer

The *Missouri Review*

CONTENTS

ESSAYS

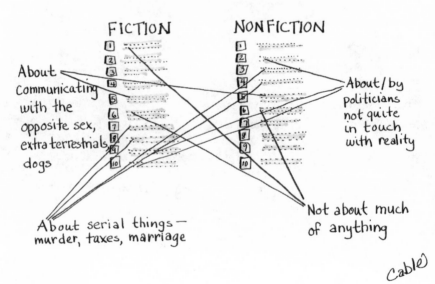

The inherent SYMMETRY
of best seller lists

FICTION   NONFICTION

About
communicating
with the
opposite sex,
extra terrestrials,
dogs

About/by
politicians
not quite
in touch
with reality

About serial things —
murder, taxes, marriage

Not about much
of anything

Cable

Foreword

Lately I have been dictating the diary that I've kept over the last thirty years. I wrote it in dozens of cheap notebooks, regularly during a few periods, but mostly very irregularly. Except for glancing at a few pages now and then, I have never read it, and in fact thought that I never would.

Reading aloud—and imagining a typist hearing—a diary kept since age twenty is not as appalling an experience as one might expect. To have stories, in a way, is to have substance, and in thirty years there will be stories, and even some of the good ones are forgotten. Reading an old diary, too, you run across occasional incidents that you have long either actively misremembered or thought of as highly important when in fact it was only one of many such events—and not even the most piquant one. What is more intriguing, however, is how much you do in fact remember but have not thought about for so long that remembering feels like successfully competing in the neurological olympics. Yes, I do remember this! one thinks, amazed that the memory is still there, unused, unlooked at, stuck away in some mental safety deposit box these twenty or thirty years.

Obviously, diaries are no less subject to cosmetic altering and outright fantasy than any other kind of writing, but the reader can usually sense it wherever it happens. While in my own diary I didn't "invent" things, I did at age twenty-one fall into occasional fits of lyrical lunacy or transparent rationalizing. By forty my diaristic rationalizing became less transparent (to me, anyway) and my lyricism had settled into mild infrequent outbreaks. Considering the fact that I didn't start the diary until leaving home, it is surprising how much it includes about my parents and the parents of friends, as if my interest in their generation went deeper than I knew.

Keeping a diary, oddly enough, serves not to intensify a person's self-involvement but the opposite, since the very act of putting things into words to some extent objectifies them. Even while the diarist writes, he is accomplishing this purpose, achieving perspective on thoughts and moods. One of the most common forms of self-imposed grief is going along with everything that pops out of the mind, so it is no small beginning to simply articulate one's experience. The great American playwright of inner turmoil and suffering, Tennessee Williams, kept a diary, and at times it was the thin paper wall keeping him from going over the edge. After a troubled student career at the University of Missouri and Washington University, Williams went to Iowa to finish his B.A. degree. While there, he wrote in his diary:

> A silly business has alienated me from the theater crowd. One of the girls had a pocket book stolen and I became quite embarrassed while they were talking about it. Was afraid they might think me guilty— *for absolutely no reason!!!*—*Idiotic*—have felt uncomfortable with them and avoided them ever since. One of the silliest things I've ever experienced. But it isn't insanity since I realize how ridiculous it is—but perhaps my queer actions have actually made them suspect me. Sounds like dementia praecox, doesn't it? [Williams sister Rose had recently been diagnosed with dementia praecox] But it's just the old guilt complex—the feeling of social inadequacy in a new guise. . . . What do I want? I want love and creative power!—eh bien! Get it?

This is a poignant example of self-observation at work, of someone choosing not to mindlessly identify with his fears and anxieties. While Williams knew that he could not simply shed his sense of "inadequacy" or magically alter his social awkwardness, at least in writing down the experience he could recognize it for what it was and set his sights beyond. In his diary Williams wrote openly about the great subjects of his plays, the flaws and sometimes pathology of families; his diary describes someone who was often simultaneously trying to escape from family, trying to understand it, yet desperately needing its support.

The connections between the generations, the imperfection of families, and the need for family are common elements in this issue of *The Missouri Review*. Mary Bush's story "Boys" depicts a pack of girlfriends on a spree, struggling through the pains and raw conflicts of discovering sexual roles and intimacy. Even as these girls are walking on a straight line away from home, they are still in the orbit, whether for good or ill, of parents and families. Leslie Daniels' "The Girl's Book of Math" is a fine, whimsical story about the sheer need for a family, a place to call home—the order of it, the caring—and the unexpected ways that families and familial roles can arise. Adam Marshall Johnson's "Watertables," set in South Dakota, concerns that time in life when the roles reverse and the young must care for the old. In "Box Seats" Tim Tomlinson writes about having a father who scares the holy hell out of you, a totally weird father, and the process of beginning to discover why he is the way he is. Finally, our previous Editors' Prize winner, David Borofka writes about the intriguing mysteries, the veils, between the generations in "How You Are Born."

E.C. Hinsey's selection of poems in this issue is about history, how to some extent we construct it by means of projections of ourselves, both personal and mythic, and what happens when those projections encounter the needs and desires of others. Walking the ruined cities of history—Budapest, Berlin, Rome, and Prague— struck by the weight of the lives lived there before, she asks the question "Who is not a witness of ruined places?" Similarly, the female character of St. Lucia in Jennifer Gage's poem sequence spreads her image across history and cultures finally into a kind of shrine, a painting that is forever being touched up in acts of revision and "redemption." In her poem "Grief" Marilyn Hacker meditates upon the real meaning of love, as she assumes the motherly role of comforting a teenaged daughter who has lost a friend in an accident.

Everyone has a personal cutoff point beyond which the past seems strange indeed, and for Norman Lavers it is growing up in a place that was an eerie mix of perfection and nightmare, described in his essay "Growing Up in Berkeley with the Bomb." Frederick Turner's essay "Shakespeare, DNA and Natural Profit" confronts an issue with widespread philosophical and economic consequences—how great a role human ingenuity should be allowed to play in influencing future generations. Turner shows that this is by no means a new problem, confined to the era of DNA discoveries, and he comes up with surprising conclusions.

*

Shakespeare is apropos to imagining what the theater was like in nineteenth-century America. Not only were Shakespeare's plays frequently staged and attended by large and varied audiences, but playhouses in America were probably more like Shakespeare's Globe than today's theaters with our quiet audiences sitting in orderly rows. In the American theaters of that time, people in the audience might be milling around, talking, initiating trysts, hissing actors they disliked off the stage, or jumping up in spontaneous, joyous approval when they liked a performance. In love with all

kinds of performing arts—music, drama, sermonizing, and oratory—
Americans were not generally receptive to understatement, subtle
effects, or staid performances. They preferred unstopping the corks
and letting the thunder roll—a style whose power we can imagine
today by listening to Martin Luther King's "I Have a Dream" speech.
At the Gettysburg commemoration, the real "speaker" for the event
was star orator Edward Everett, who held forth for a typical two-
hour display of oratorical fireworks, while President Lincoln's few
quiet words, spoken afterward, were indeed little noted at the time,
despite being long remembered.

An "American style" of dramatic performance had clearly emerged
as early as the 1830s, with actors like Junius Booth—progenitor of a big
family of actors, including the infamous John Wilkes—who rejected
the "English style" of performance in favor of a tempestuous style.
Booth's acting was cave-man Stanislavsky: he became so involved in
his roles that in swordfights he ran actors into the street, when he
played Lear his skin turned scarlet, as Othello he nearly smothered
Desdemona, and he quite often genuinely frightened other actors
as well as audiences.

Theaters, like movies today, were driven by the compulsion to fill
the seats with sentimental formulas staged and acted with melo-
dramatic excess. It is not surprising that under these circumstances,
nineteenth-century American playwrights did not produce elegant
masterpieces. Mark Twain's play "Colonel Sellers," published for
the first time in this issue of *The Missouri Review*, is no exception. The
play ran for many years and earned Twain more money than any
other literary property during his lifetime. It is in some ways rep-
resentative of the era: sentimental, loosely constructed, populated
by stock characters. It is also typical of much of Twain's writing
with its open reaching for commercial popularity. Yet despite that,
it shows the stamp of genius in the leading role of Colonel Sellers,
who is—all by himself—an American comic classic.

SM

BOYS / *Mary Bush*

HERE THEY WERE NOW walking down the dark road with the chirping crickets and the earthy smell of the fields, of corn coming up sharp and rich, hitting them so they gasped, they really did once in a while, even though it was a faint smell, but it clung, it was a gauze curtain, it was everywhere. Once they got farther out of town there was the sharp odor of onions, too, rising from the muckland, *the muck* they called it, and the humidity hanging in the air, and the warmth inside them from beer and gin and vodka, and still the night was not over. It was just beginning.

The three of them kicking up stones on the shoulder of the farm road that led far out of town while the farmers slept in their beds under cool sheets, while their parents slept, while their little brothers and sisters and the people who worked in the bank and the grocery store and the old lady with the hump back and their teachers and the priest and even most of the dogs and cats slept, they walked in the dark heading into the muckland because they had made a plan, a pact. They had all sneaked out of their houses to meet in Barbara's barn—a storage shed, really—to smoke cigarettes and drink beer and gin and vodka they'd stolen from their parents and get drunk and then walk out to the old Granger house, where they would meet boys. Barbara walked because she was part of the group, she was part of them, they were all in it together, and they had all hung out together for a long time, at least three years, maybe four years, and people called them bad girls, but they didn't know, didn't know anything about them— her and Marie, her best friend, and Nita who was strange and Gussie—the old crow—who was funny and fun to be with but serious, too, and still afraid of her parents, well her father at least, and that's why she wasn't with them. In spirit she was with them. Every time they had a drink they had another one for Gussie.

Barbara stumbled with them past Sullivan's creek where the last farmhouse stood next to a wide pasture, its lone black tree a shadow against the sky, and the water gurgling down below them, and the dank smell of mud, and here they were on the road, laughing, bumping into each other as they walked. It was okay because it was an accident, they were drunk, they could bump arms over and over, and Marie's arm was warm and soft and she never moved, she just let Barbara fall into her, lean against her because it was night and they were best friends and they were drunk.

I wanna dance with you, they sang. *I wanna dance with you.*

But then Nita was so depressed. She started telling them about it, how Larry didn't like her, she was sure he didn't like her, he liked some other girl, and she lit a cigarette while she told them what a bastard he was, how he'd led her along, the shit, and now she wished he was dead. And if he showed up tonight at the Granger house, if he was there like he said he'd be (though she didn't expect him), don't think for a minute she was going to act like she liked him, not after the way he treated her. Just let him try to act like he liked her and see what happened.

The cigarette trembled in her mouth as she tried to talk with it, because that was cool, that was what cool women alcoholics did and she was trying to keep cool, but the cigarette fell, and she couldn't pick it up, she kept missing it, and then she bent over again to reach for it and she fell.

Oh shit, she said, as she lay there on the side of the road, her arms spread out. Oh shit, look at me—and they stopped and looked.

Nita got to her knees, then stood, then stumbled, pretending she was drunker than she was—anybody could see she was putting on a show, she'd hardly had anything to drink—and she flung herself into the ditch while Barbara and Marie watched her.

I wish I was dead, she said from the ditch. Oh, I'm so sick. I'm dying.

Get out of there, Marie told her. Stop fooling around.

I can't move, she said. I'm dying.

Come on, they said. We don't have all night.

Finally they stumbled down into the ditch and took her arms, and Barbara felt so close to Marie because they were working together, they knew Nita was being an ass and they had to put up with her together, and they took her arms and pulled her to her feet. Nita smiled and let her head flop.

I'm so drunk.

Of course she was putting it all on, and Barbara and Marie just looked at each other, and the look said We're in this together. See what we have to put up with?

When they got Nita back on the road they gave her a little push to get her moving, and then they let go of her and they started walking ahead of her, faster, because Nita was always pulling something just to get attention, this wasn't the first time, and you could see right through her.

Just to dance with you.

They were going to start a rock band together, a girl rock band, and they'd be famous, everybody would be jealous and want to get to know them, and they'd meet all the big rock stars, and make some albums and get on tv, the only all-girl rock band in the world. They called themselves Birds of a Feather, and Barbara played rhythm guitar a little bit, and Marie tried guitar but couldn't do it, so maybe if they found a bass she could play bass, but mostly she'd just sing because she was pretty, and people could look at her, the best-looking one, and Nita, the rag doll, you couldn't count on her even though she said she wanted to play drums, but Gussie played drums, so they weren't sure yet how many were really in the band, they still had a few things to work out, like learning to play their instruments better, and finding a time to practice together, and learning some songs, and getting some equipment, and finding a place that would hire them to play. Once people found out about them, they'd all want to join, so they had to keep it a secret for now, at least until they got better and made some money and maybe got on the radio.

Barbara figured some day it would be just her and Marie singing and playing, a duo, but who cared if the band never really got going as long as the two of them could stay together. Duos were popular, there were duos all over the place, tons of them getting famous. Though a rock band, a *band*, would be a really good idea.

Marie leaned close, she leaned into Barbara all on her own, Barbara hadn't had to do a thing to make it happen. She just kept walking with Marie's arm pressed against her, breathing, barely breathing. And they were alone in the wide stretch of farmland, not a barn, not a house in sight, only a tree poking up here and there, and the night sky above with its pale half moon, something soft and hazy covering them.

You know, I didn't tell you, Marie said—whispered—her breath so warm and soft on Barbara's ear. It was hard for her to talk. She was mumbling, trying to say something you could see was hard to say, just for Barbara, not for Nita to hear, and Barbara breathed in ever so softly, holding it, holding her breath.

What?

I didn't tell you—you know—I saw Miles today.

Miles, the boy who was after Marie. The boy Marie liked. The new boy who'd just moved to town a few months ago. His face was just a little chubby, and he had short curly hair and yellow teeth, and he was always smiling with his mouth open so you had to look at his yellow teeth, and he wasn't very smart, and nobody knew anything about him except his parents had put him in some kind of reformatory run by priests, but nobody knew why or even if it was true, but he was here now, living in this town with both his parents and his brother and Marie liked him.

Yeah? she said, trying to sound like she meant it, how nice, what a surprise, wow, he must really like you—

But it was weird, Marie said, whispered, leaning close to Barbara, finding it hard to talk, to say the words, while Nita stumbled along behind them crying, Oh, I'm drunk I can't stand up, help me, but they wouldn't even turn around to look at her.

Weird. That was good, that was better, because weird sounded like something was wrong, and now Barbara could be there for Marie to confide in, it would make them that much closer.

What do you mean, she asked. What do you mean, weird?

I don't know, Marie answered, and they walked along, bumping into each other, silently, with Nita mumbling Wait for me, I'm sick, I'm drunk, something's wrong with my legs.

What? Barbara said. What was so weird?

Marie shook her head and sniffed—It's just—and their arms touched, then parted.

You got any cigarettes left? she asked Barbara.

Yes, Barbara had cigarettes. She carried them because they all smoked, even though smoke made her dizzy, and no matter how much she tried she could not get used to it.

Here, she told Marie, pulling a cigarette out of the pack and handing it to her, letting their fingers brush against each other. She watched Marie take it, her hands trembling, her hair falling into her face so that she had to brush it back with her hand, and then swing her head to the side to make the hair fling back over her shoulder, with the white cigarette dangling from her lips, and her eyes narrowed and looking ahead at the road.

They had to stop. They had to stand still while Barbara found her pack of matches and Nita caught up with them and made her knees buckle and sank to the ground.

I think I'm paralyzed, she said. My legs.

Barbara held the book of matches, considering—should she hand Marie the book, or should she strike the match herself and hold it out for Marie? If she struck the match and held it out, Marie would take Barbara's hand and hold it steady while her cigarette was being lit, and their eyes would meet, their eyes would meet over the flame, and something—that aching, painful, delicious feeling—would pass between them. Even though girls never did such a thing for each other, never lit each other's cigarettes, only boys did that for girls. But maybe Marie was drunk enough for it to be all right.

Marie stood with the cigarette dangling, looking ahead down the dark road, thinking, something on her mind, the weird thing on her mind, waiting for Barbara to get the matches, and she reached her hand out to take the book which Barbara was starting to open.

Here, you want me to—

Marie swinging her hair, looking down at the book of matches. Yeah, I need a match. Taking the book, the bent, almost torn-out match, from Barbara, their two hands fumbling over the little square piece of cardboard.

Barbara drank in the picture, Marie in the moonlight tearing off the match, striking it, so cool, and there, a circle of light framing her, a small brightness in the night, her blonde hair flung over her shoulder, her face concentrated and distracted, something on her mind, lighting the match and holding it to the tip of the cigarette, the end of the cigarette glowing red, then the shake of the wrist, again, again, the match out.

Help me up, I'm paralyzed, my legs.

They turned to look at Nita sprawled on the ground, a rag doll. Then Nita laughing, crying: I'm drunk.

Get up and stop fooling around, Marie told her. She grabbed Nita's arms and yanked her up. We're going to leave you here if you don't stop it.

They started walking again, the three of them, Nita moaning Shit, oh shit. I hate Larry.

Then everything was quiet for a while as they walked, no houses now, just the sharp pungent onion fields and the silence, except for the sound of their feet scuffing the ground, and the droning insects, and their breathing, and Marie drawing in on the cigarette, then holding it, then letting the air out, Barbara breathing with her.

It was so weird, Marie said. I wanted to tell you.

But then they reached the run-down old gray house set back from the road, weeds high all around it, the muck fields behind it.

They're not here yet? Marie said.

Thank God they're not here yet, Barbara thought.

They're not coming, Nita said. At least Larry. I know Larry's not coming. I hope he doesn't think I'm expecting him or anything, because I'm not.

She wasn't drunk anymore, and she wasn't paralyzed. She was standing on the side of the road looking at the tall weeds and the Granger house saying He can just go to hell, that's what he can do.

Should we go up there, Marie asked. You think we should go up to the porch or something?

They looked for a path and found one, though it wasn't very wide. This grass, Nita said, swatting at it. I hope there aren't any snakes in here.

They looked up at the sky, the tree tops, and put their hands to their heads as they made their way to the porch, spread them to cover their hair.

The house was big and dark, and you could smell it, rats and squirrels and raccoon nests and all kinds of awful things behind the boarded-up windows. Dead animals, beer and wine bottles from kids partying out there, chunks of wood lathe and plaster kicked out of the walls, you could feel it behind you without even looking, the big empty boarded-up creepy house.

They sat on the porch and lit cigarettes and waited for the boys to show up in Miles' car that he said his father bought him after he got out of the reformatory or whatever it was. The paint on the wooden porch felt rough, bubbled and peeling and crumbly, and they picked at it and pulled strips of paint up and tossed them over the side of the porch while they waited. And all the while Marie looked at Barbara with those eyes that said If Nita wasn't here I could talk to you.

They wondered what time it was. They wished they had some beer. They wondered how they would get home if the boys did not show up, since it was a long way back to town and they were tired and they swore they were not walking all the way back there, no way.

I know he's not going to show up, Nita said. I know Larry's not going to show up, I just know it. She lay back on the porch and waved her hands in the air above her, then dropped her arms with a thud to her sides. I wish I was dead, she said.

They were going to go driving, that's all, driving with the boys, and smoking, and drinking and then they'd go parking and they'd make out for a while, Marie would, that is, with Miles who was new, who had just come into the picture not too long ago, and Nita would, with Larry if he came, which he might, even though Nita swore he wouldn't. But Barbara would not make out, there would be no boy for her—thank God for that. She was happy to hang out with her girlfriends, just her and her girlfriends, that's the way it had always been. Who would've ever thought it would change? Who would've thought Marie would get a boyfriend? Nita, maybe, maybe even Gussie, if her father would ever let her go out, even though she went out anyway sometimes, they might get boyfriends. Nita already had a boyfriend, Larry, though Larry didn't like Nita, but not Marie, not her best friend Marie who could lean into her, who could touch her arm and keep it there, who could touch her face—jokingly, of course, grab her cheek and shake it jokingly, but touch her face just the same.

I've gotta pee, Nita said, and she sat up and looked around. Don't you guys have to pee after all we drank?

No, they didn't have to, they didn't know why, they just didn't.

Nita stood up. Well, I'm gonna take a leak. And she started down the steps and stopped and looked over at the tall weeds. I hope there aren't any snakes in there.

If there are, they're all asleep, Marie told her.

Don't look, Nita said. I don't want to go too far away, so don't look.

She went around the side of the house, they could hear her rustling through the grass, stepping on twigs, talking to them about the scratchy weeds and snakes and poison ivy.

Marie sat hunched over, looking into her lap, then at the floor between her and Barbara, and Barbara felt them alone in the night inches away from each other, and it came back, the thing that Marie hadn't been able to say. Marie straightened up a little and looked at Barbara with those pleading eyes, so that Barbara wanted to cry out What? What is it?

Marie laughed, embarrassed, shook her head.

You know that dirt road that goes to Patrini's warehouse? Off Buck Road where all the trailers are?

Yes, Barbara knew the road.

Yeah, I know it. Though she'd never been there. She'd hardly even been on Buck Road. Who'd ever go on Buck Road with all those trailers and barking dogs?

Miles took me there, to Patrini's warehouse, Marie said. Today. She lowered her head and looked in her lap, then raised her head and shook it, looked in Barbara's eyes, laughed.

You went in the warehouse?

After Miles got off work.

Boys, Barbara thought. She knew why boys would take a girl into a warehouse, she'd heard them talk, her cousins, boys at school. There was only one reason a boy would take a girl into a warehouse, especially Patrini's warehouse at the end of a dirt road off scumbag Buck Road.

You're kidding, Barbara said.

Marie nodded her head yes, yes he did, he really did. It was so strange. She'd never thought—never thought—and she lowered her voice so that her voice disappeared, it dropped into her lap, and everything was quiet, even Nita, wherever she was.

So that was the awful thing that Marie had been trying to say.

What happened? Barbara said.

He.... Well, it was weird, standing up, against some smelly onion crates, kissing.

Kissing. They'd kissed plenty of times in front of Barbara. That's what they did together, kissed, and all Barbara could think of was those yellow teeth pressing against Marie's mouth, against her white teeth, the pink inside of her mouth. Did it even cross his mind, even once, to brush his teeth?

Yeah? Barbara said.

And it was hard for Marie to talk again, to say the words that wanted to come out, so that Barbara had to think What? What? Don't tell me he *did* it to her? Because none of them had ever done it with a boy, though everybody in school thought they were bad girls, not really bad, not the kind that screwed around all over the place, really, but bad enough, the kind that went out drinking and driving and parking and making out with boys, the kind parents would make a worried face over and shake their heads over.

Yeah? Barbara said.

Marie slid closer to Barbara on the rough, peeling porch floor, and Barbara could hear the wood and paint snagging on Marie's shorts.

Marie leaned closer and looked at Barbara like she couldn't believe what had happened, what she was about to say had happened.

He took it out, she said. (Such a long pause after she said it.) He told me to touch it.

Barbara looked at Marie, just looked at those eyes of hers that said she still could not believe what had happened.

Did you? Barbara asked, trying to make her voice sound like it was no big deal.

But she was falling, talking to Marie from deep inside some hole she hadn't even known was there.

Marie was crying. Softly, quietly—not like Nita who was always such an ass when she cried, you could tell in two seconds she was faking it. But Marie was really crying, and it brought Barbara back up into the air a little bit.

He made me touch it, Marie said. I didn't want to.

Made you?

Well, told me to, he didn't make me.

It was awful, Marie talking to her about her and Miles alone together, alone in the dark, touching, *touching* like that.

I didn't know they got that big, Marie said, and she gave a little laugh, then sniffled.

Miles with the yellow teeth and the short curly hair and the pudgy round shoulders. Barbara couldn't picture it.

He told me to touch it, Marie sniffed.

That's all you did? Barbara asked her. Touched it?

Of course, Marie said, surprised. Of course.

Bad girls, Barbara thought. Everybody thought they were bad girls, though they weren't, not at all, but it was strange, really strange that Marie would get so upset, that she'd *cry* over seeing one or touching one, and it was her boyfriend, besides, somebody who slobbered all over her mouth all the time. It wasn't like some guy she didn't know had grabbed her and made her do it. But just the idea, the idea that everybody thought they were girls like that, that they had a reputation, and here Marie was crying over just seeing her boyfriend's dick. It was such a joke.

Barbara shook her head, watching Marie sniffle and wipe her nose, and listening to Nita crackle through the weeds on her way back.

I didn't want Nita to know, Marie whispered.

Okay, Barbara said. But—you still want to see him now? You still want to see Miles tonight?

Marie blew her nose. I guess so.

And that was all there was to it. Marie, her best friend. They knew everything in the world about each other—well, almost everything. But this was something else, Marie crying and upset but still wanting to see Miles, and there was nothing Barbara could do about it, so she may as well not even think about it, not even try. Except how could she not try?

Nita climbed back onto the porch. I threw up, too, she told them. I told you I was sick. She flung herself onto the porch beside them.

There's a used drum set at the music store we can get, Barbara told them, meaning Marie, Marie, come back. We could start our band.

I know how to play drums. Nita said. *Well my heart went boom when I crossed the room.* I'm going to play the drums.

But she was lying, of course, and nobody wanted her to play drums, nobody even really wanted her in the band at all because she was such a big pain. Besides, Gussie was supposed to play drums.

We could practice in my barn, at least till winter, Barbara told them.

Or my house, Nita said. In my cellar.

But Marie was looking out at the road, waiting for the boys to come. How are we supposed to get money to buy a drum set? she asked Barbara while looking down the road.

We can sell things, Barbara told her. Hold a raffle. Or a bake sale or something.

My cousin's got a drum set, Nita said. I play his drum set all the time. I can play the drums really good. She started drumming out a beat on the porch floor to prove how good she was.

Nita pounded the floor, then slapped her foot to make the cymbals crash.

Is that headlights? Marie said, and they all looked down the road, straining to see, and there it was, far away, a faint light blinking through clumps of whatever grew alongside the road, and then finally the sound of a car in the humid night air.

Marie stood up and brushed off the seat of her shorts.

I know Larry's not with him, Nita said. I just know it.

And now the worst part begins, Barbara thought. She had already had her night, and now it was over, but she would have to stay with them while they drove around and went parking, and it was awful, she'd done it a couple of other times and she hated it. But she couldn't let Marie know that she wished there was no such thing as boys, no such thing for that matter as Miles Dwight Walker from who-knows-what reformatory or what town or why his family had moved here, it all sounded fishy to her.

The car chugged closer, the headlights shone brighter.

Nita stood up. I know he's not here, she said.

The car honked and veered off the road, spitting gravel and rocking to a stop at the edge of the tall weeds, the headlights shining towards the porch, but missing it by about three feet, lighting up instead a rotting stack of firewood and the tall grass around it and a prickly thistle bush. They could hear music, the radio, coming from the car. Miles shut off the engine and two boys got out and slammed their doors and started towards them.

I told you he wouldn't come, Nita said, and you could hear her voice, almost crying, but interested too, wondering who the new boy was.

Barbara started slipping, back down into the terrible hole, because the boys were really here and now everything would change.

Miles waved his hand at them, dumbly. Just about everything he did was dumb, and the other boy who was not Larry stumbled along behind him in the grass.

They reached the porch and Miles said "'Lo" in that dumb stupid way of his, like he was too stupid to talk, all he could do was grunt like a farmhand, and he may as well have been one, because that's what he looked like and acted like, somebody who'd just stumbled out of a cow barn with manure all over his shoes and straw and mud stuck to his clothes.

He walked over to Marie and within two seconds, right before Barbara's eyes, Marie's face turned dumb and puffy, her shoulders slumped forward, and she laughed the way she always did when she was around Miles. She giggled and watched him like a little dog waiting for its owner to tell it what stupid trick to do next— sit up, roll over—well maybe not that bad, but it was sickening just the same. Now Marie stood far apart from Barbara. Now she did not bump into her or brush her arm or hand against her, and she did not look with big surprised eyes at Barbara or lean her face close and whisper. She stood far apart from Barbara and waited for Miles to come to her.

And Nita was worse, or would have been worse if Larry was there, but she was bad enough because it was a boy, any boy, and she acted like an idiot. Hi, Nita said, her nose in the air like a ratty dog sniffing out another dog. Hi, like this boy had been brought just for her but she had to sniff him out to make sure she wanted him, and Miles said Oh, yeah, this is—whatever his name was, Joe or Jim or Jack—and the boy stuffed his hands in his pockets and swayed and said Hi, looking Nita up and down, because this was all something he might go for, he wasn't sure yet.

Barbara watched them, taking in every breath and movement, how it was all so different, even the sound of their voices, high and pinched when a boy was around. Miles walked right up to Marie and she leaned into him, put her arms around him while he didn't even notice, while he looked out across at the rest of them with his eyes narrowed and his mouth open, smiling, satisfied, *King of the roost*, her mother would have called him. Then Miles kissed Marie—her looking up at him the whole time, waiting for him to do it—while he looked over at Nita and the other boy, not even paying attention to kissing Marie, like he was already tired of it, or bored, and she put her arms around his chubby shoulders tighter and started kissing him back, letting him know how much he meant to her. After a little while Miles stopped looking at the others and put his arms around Marie, and everybody had to stand there waiting and watching until they were done kissing.

Touch it, Barbara thought. In a hot stuffy onion warehouse pushing her up against a stack of onion crates, sticking his tongue into her mouth, unzipping his pants and taking it out and saying, There, touch it. And Marie—what? Had she said, Oh no! Please, not that? Or had she leaned into his arms and whispered Yes, I want to. Had she acted like she'd done it before, like it was all perfectly normal, so that Miles thought she wanted to do it, liked to do it? And then crying about it to Barbara.

You got anything to drink? Miles asked them.

Oh—Marie was ready to fall to the ground and shrivel up over it. No beer for Miles, no vodka or gin.

She giggled, not the Marie Barbara knew. We thought you guys'd have something, she told Miles.

But you could hear how terrible it was for her, not having any booze to give Miles.

I got so drunk, Nita told them.

Yeah? the new boy said, lifting his head.

I fell in the ditch, Nita told him.

No shit, he said, looking her up and down.

All's we got left is half a quart of beer in the car, Miles said. Piss warm. And all the stores are closed.

It was too bad. They stood looking at each other, because how could you go out driving in the middle of the night and then go parking if you didn't have something to drink, if you couldn't get drunk?

At least now maybe they could go home, Barbara thought, just drive them home and say goodnight, and maybe she'd only have to watch Miles and Marie kissing a little bit before it was over.

Besides, they were all so stupid when they were drunk. They were stupid enough when they weren't drunk.

"We gotta get some booze," Miles said.

"We should break into that liquor store in town," the new boy said. "I can pick a lock like nothing."

Miles looked at him for a minute, thinking about it. "You're crazy," he said. "You got a smoke?" he asked Marie.

Suddenly Marie remembered Barbara, turned to Barbara, took a step closer to her to ask for a cigarette for Miles, and Barbara hated him. I hate him, she thought. He's a stupid pig with yellow teeth and his mouth is always open.

I don't know, she told Marie. I don't know if I have any left. She opened her purse and felt around inside, felt the half-full pack, felt herself divide, get ripped in two, a terrible pain, wanting to please Marie, do anything for her, hating Miles, not wanting to give him even a piece of dirty lint from the inside of her purse.

I think I'm all out, she told Marie, but she kept feeling the insides of her purse, the kleenex and compact and sticks of gum, the nail file and comb and marbles and lint. When she looked up she saw Marie's pleading eyes in the dim moonlight, please oh please have one stinking measly little cigarette left—all the gold in the world, all the jewels on earth—that I can give to my prince, my god, my king of the roost, the one I would crawl in the dirt for, I would lick the bottoms of his farmer shoes for, Miles Dwight Walker, oh please, so he will love me for a cigarette.

I don't think I have any left, Barbara told her, squeezing her fingers around the half-full pack.

You should have never gotten out of that reformatory, she thought. Why can't you just go back where you belong and leave us alone?

But she would do anything for Marie, anything, and she felt her hand slowly slowly coming out of her purse, holding the pack, and she said words she did not want to say—Here—maybe, I think . . .

And Marie's face lit up, sending a sword through Barbara because it was, yes, such a look of love, but the love was not for her. It was love for the cigarette she could give to Miles.

You found some, Marie cried. You found some after all.

Barbara handed over the cigarette and matches to Miles, and they all watched Miles light a cigarette and take a big puff and then drop the burning match without putting it out.

Thanks, he said. To Marie, not Barbara.

Miles blew smoke out his yellow teeth, then pulled Marie close, Marie laughing, the two of them kissing like that, with Miles smoking, blowing smoke into her mouth as they kissed. Well, it was something to do, something different so he didn't have to get so bored kissing her.

It made her sick, actually sick in her stomach, to watch them kissing and running their hands up and down each other. Nita and Joe or Jim or Jack were sitting on the porch steps, leaning against each other. He had his arm around her waist, and he was pulling her close though she looked like she was leaning away from him at the same time. He was telling Nita about last winter, how he dropped out of school and hitchhiked to Arizona.

Really? Wow.

Yeah, and what did his mother care? And his old man, he was worse, he didn't give a shit, to hell with them anyway, and he'd worked on some ranch, but you had to watch out for the Mexicans, because he'd had his wallet stolen, his driver's license, and once he'd been hit over the head and knocked out by a drunk Mexican, he figured that's what the guy was, anyway, since they were all over the place, and another time he'd been stabbed, but it was okay there in Arizona, except it got too hot, so he figured he'd come back north for the summer, what the hell. You wanna smoke some pot? I got one joint left.

Barbara saw it all.

But then Miles peered over at Barbara, and his mouth stopped grinning, and their eyes met for just a second. He started walking away with Marie, holding her, his arm around her waist, whispering to Marie, but Barbara heard him: You couldn't get rid of her? That load of deadwood?

I tried, Marie whispered back. Just drop her off, okay?

Barbara's whole body stopped cold, Marie's words echoing in the air: I *tried*.

So stunned she could not move.

Let's get out of here, Miles said, moving towards the car holding Marie around the waist, smoking what was left of Barbara's cigarette, and Joe or Jim or Jack stood up and pulled Nita to her feet and she fell into him, giggling, because, of course she was suddenly drunk again, or starting to get paralyzed, or something. Anyway she needed help standing up straight, and she needed help walking, so he put his arm around her waist, and she put her arm around his neck so that it looked like she would choke him and they started walking to the car, too. Barbara stumbled through the weeds behind them.

She'd driven around with them before, with the boys not speaking one word to her, and her own girlfriends not even speaking to her because they were too busy kissing the boys or paying attention to every stupid word the boys said so they could laugh and giggle in just the right places, and she was used to it, sort of. But never this—never had she heard them say one word about her. And Marie, Marie too?

They got in the car, Miles and Marie up front, Nita and the new boy in back practically in each other's laps and Barbara against the door in back, her head pressed to the frame of the open window, and they started kissing again, taking forever about it, and she hated them. She hated the stupid sounds they made, the sucking and sighing and tugging of their sticky bodies against the vinyl seats, hated them for making her sit there trapped in the car listening, waiting for Miles to start the car and get going —to *drop her off.*

Just take me home and drop me off so this night can be over, she thought. But he did not start the car. Instead, the new boy took out the marijuana and they sat with the windows rolled up and handed the last joint around. Barbara took two little puffs just to show them, no matter what they thought about her, while she waited, waited for them to get going. It was so hot and stuffy and sickly sweet in the car.

Your folks must have some vodka or something, Miles told Marie. But no, there was no vodka, nothing.

Then to Nita: How about you? You said your mother was a drunk.

She *is*, Nita said. That's why there's nothing left. Then the sound of her laughing, giggling, because it was so funny, she was so clever, it was really amazing, but when nobody else laughed she stopped.

Just take me home, Barbara thought. Just start the car and go.

Marie turning, asking her, just in case, asking because Miles would not talk to her, not even for something as important as getting drunk. But Barbara had already taken the bottle of gin that had been in the house since she could remember.

Shit, Miles said. What kind of town is this, anyways?

Then Marie, that beautiful face, that smile, almost shy, all for Barbara, just for her, telling Barbara: That guy your uncle knows. The one who makes wine.

An old man Barbara never thought about, a man she hardly knew.

Oh, Barbara said.

He keeps it in the cellar, Marie announced, and Barbara cringed.

Well, shit, the new boy said, looking up and pushing Nita a few inches away from him. Now you're talking.

Miles started the engine, and they lurched onto the road.

He drove fast, with the radio playing, their windows open again, and the warm humid farm air rushing in through the open windows while Marie gave him directions to the man's house in the little tract near the highway, the house Barbara had told Marie about once, just for something to talk about, just because it was different. After all, how many kids knew people who made wine?

I'm not going in there, Barbara thought to herself. I have nothing to do with this, nothing at all.

Shit, the new boy said. This shit better be good.

They pulled into the housing tract and drove slowly along the dim street. Only a few lights were on.

Isn't that it? Marie asked.

The house Barbara had only been inside of once, dark. She would die if he ever found out. If her family found out.

Yeah, Barbara told Marie. But—

You go in, Miles told Barbara. Since you know the place.

Talking to her now, friendly, happy even, Barbara his old friend, his best friend in the whole world, Barbara. *Deadwood.*

I can't, Barbara told them, trying to picture it, trying to see herself sneaking into someone's cellar in the middle of the night, touching his things, taking his wine, while he slept with his wife upstairs, dreaming, an old man, somebody her family knew. I can't, she told them.

What the hell's wrong with you? the new boy said. What'd you bring us here for, then, for Christ sake?

I didn't, Barbara told him. Because she didn't, she hadn't brought them there, hadn't said a word.

Barbara shook her head at them.

Hell, the new boy said. I'll go, then. Just tell me where the hell to go.

The cellar, stupid, Miles said from the front seat. Didn't you hear us say cellar a hundred times already?

So how the hell do I get in the cellar?

I think it's in back, Marie told him. The door. Isn't it in back? she asked.

Yes, it was in back, yes the outside entrance to the cellar was in back, yes of course she'd told Marie all about it one time, not that either of them even liked wine, though her father said the old man's wine wasn't so bad, but she was going to have absolutely nothing to do with this whole thing, nothing at all, she decided, while Marie looked at her, waiting, all of them waiting for an answer, and angry, as if she'd done something to them.

Yeah, Barbara finally told Marie.

The new boy opened the car door.

Just don't make any noise, Miles told him.

I can do this with my eyes closed, the kid told them.

Shut up, Miles said, or you'll wake up the whole town.

Barbara held her breath, dying inside. She watched the new boy stumble across the old man's yard, then disappear around the back, and it made her sick that he was there, he had no right to be on the property, and she hoped the police would come along and arrest him, all of them, except she was there too with them. She put her hand on the door handle, thinking she would leave, but she was afraid to leave Marie with them, those boys, those criminals, intruders.

Marie and Miles watching out the window, whispering to each other about the kid, about whether he'd found the door and whether he was tripping over things, getting them all in trouble.

Jesus, Nita said. What's taking him so long?

I will wait ten more seconds, Barbara thought. I will count to ten slowly and then if he's not here I will open the door and walk home.

I will count to ten one more time, she told herself.

And then the boy was running around the corner, a bottle in each hand, racing for the car, jumping inside yelling Go, get the hell out of here.

Did they hear you? Miles asked, hitting the gas, the car pulling away with the boy's door swinging open, and Barbara looking back, letting out her breath just as the car turned the corner and a light went on in the house.

They were laughing, driving out on the highway, relieved, listening to the new kid tell about it, tell about knocking over a jar or something, hearing it crash in the cellar, hearing a bed creak upstairs, footsteps, just as his hands went around the bottles. It was great, man, great, I feel great, he said.

But shit, fuck. The bottles had *corks*.

Marie fumbling through the glove compartment while Miles

steered the car back off the highway, back the way they'd come, telling her where to look in the glove compartment, what to look for, a metal bottle opener with a hinge on it, a corkscrew attachment, he was sure it was in there.

And Barbara's stomach, that awful feeling like a bad dream, seeing again and again the pale light blinking on in the old man's house as they turned the corner.

And now she was nothing again, nothing to them, as they fumbled to open their bottles of wine, and the car roared out on the other side of town, over near the muckland where they had been walking and now they passed the bottle around, drinking, and Marie leaned her face into Miles' neck and Nita and the new boy made sucking huffing sounds on the other end of the back seat. Never, she thought, I will never do what they are doing.

And she didn't even have to say a word, she knew exactly where Miles was heading now: to her house where he would dump her, where he and Marie together would get rid of her, because she had had her one moment of almost being of any use to them, and now she was nothing again. If she just looked out the window into the black night with the shadowy fields and the dark trees lining the ditches, if she just breathed the air, pretty soon it would be over and she would be home in bed and it would be like this night had never happened.

And then the next day or the next, whenever she saw Marie again, Marie would tell her things, confide in her, maybe talk about Miles in the warehouse saying touch it, maybe talk about Nita, what a pain she was, what were they going to do with her, maybe talk about holding a raffle, buying the drum set and starting their band, or maybe not, maybe she wouldn't talk about that anymore, but she'd talk like she always had, just the two of them, best friends forever, nothing would ever change that ever.

No, she told herself. No, no.

She was in the car alone, that's all she knew. Except she knew that things had gone too far. They've gone too far, she thought as she looked out into the passing fields, this thing about boys, this thing with boys, with Marie and boys, and Nita and boys, even though she didn't really like Nita, and with Gussie and boys, too, if her father would ever let her out of the house. With all of Barbara's girlfriends and boys. Marie, acting like they were best friends, then telling Miles: *I tried to get rid of her. Just drop her off.*

It wasn't going to stop, she thought.

Marie was a little boat on the sea, a twig floating down the stream, away from her. Marie her best friend, who had hardly spoken a word to her since Miles showed up, except to get things from her for Miles, Marie who didn't even know that she existed anymore, who had tried to get rid of her. It drained her, emptied her, it made her numb and hollow in the terrible hot night.

The car slowed, rounding a curve, coming into town where they would drop her off, and out in the field near Sullivan's creek stood that single tree, leafless, its branches sparse and broken. Poor dead tree, Barbara thought, in the middle of all this land, the cow pastures and weeds and open fields. She felt her throat burn, and her eyes begin to tear.

She pressed her face to the edge of the window, and she hated them, all of them, even Marie, Marie who she could hate worst of all.

Mary Bush is a past winner of *MR*'s William Peden Prize for the title story of her collection, *A Place of Light*.

"This just in — the food police are now targeting the recent novels of Cormac McCarthy."

HOW YOU ARE BORN / *David Borofka*

MIRANDA LAMBERT'S BEDROOM WAS on the third floor of the family's manor house, overlooking the sweep of the back lawn, the reflecting pool, the twin gazebos and the rose garden. During the winter the view was not remarkable; mist obscured the details of the scene like a painting that has been overworked, and clouds provided such a low ceiling as to make a submariner claustrophobic. In winter the drapes were rarely opened, but in summer, during those moments when the overcast was suspended, the picture from her leaded glass windows was something out of a fairy tale, including the beauties of the back half of the estate as well as the Olympian triangle of Mount Hood.

Today the drapes were open, but she was not admiring the landscape. She was, instead, trying to teach me the intricacies of a card game called Hell Bridge. With little success, I might add. It was some variation of Rummy or Michigan Kitty that the Lambert family played, but Mira was not a normal girl, and her explanation of the rules sounded like something out of Lewis Carroll. I could make no sense of it.

"You're not trying, Fish," she said, "this isn't geometry or logarithms."

"I know it's not." I stifled a yawn. "Freddy had me up all night."

The night before, at midnight, her brother had shaken me out of a fitful sleep to invite me to a party down by the river. He opened the window of my room and showed me the way across the slate roof and down the trellis on the south side of the house to the ground. Freddy was two years older, had recently obtained his driver's license, and I was flattered that he would include me. Only later did I realize that he had invited me because my bedroom window was his only escape route.

Our way was lighted by a fickle moon that played tag with the clouds. At one moment the path along the roof was outlined as clearly as day, the next we were feeling our way toward the edge where nothing separated the roof from the ground but air. Then down the trellis, clutching the ivy, and across the back lawn, sprinting like burglars from one shadowed border to the other.

"No, no, no," Mira was saying, "a run of four has to be in the same suit."

"You said they had to be in sequence."

"*And* in the same suit," she huffed. "Honestly, Fish."

"Don't be snotty."

"Don't be stupid."

I swallowed one more enormous yawn, then stretched out on the braided rug. As large and as elevated as her bedroom was, the only habitable room on the third floor, it was not a fourteen-year-old girl's pink-and-cream fantasy. The wallpaper was peeling off plaster walls that were themselves crumbling, wind whistled through the casements and down the chimney of her fireplace, and a person could easily pick up splinters from the hardwood floor. In the center of an ornate rose medallion, an unshaded bulb dangled from an archaic wire. By comparison, on the floor below, the room that I had been assigned had been completely redone: paint, floors, fixtures, the works.

Mira's mother had told me that her room was the last of the Lambert house to be renovated. Mira had so far frustrated her mother's efforts, saying that she liked her room as it was, but Mrs. Lambert was closing in. I was reminded of my father's aunt who near the end of her days became convinced that the nuclear threat was imminent and, claiming that her twenty-three-room house was too big a target, chose to live in the detached garage. Mira's stubbornness seemed no less eccentric than my great-aunt's fright.

"This place is a dump," I said. "You ought to let your mother fix it."

"My mother isn't going to get within ten feet of this room." Mira held the deck of cards in her right hand, flexing them in the direction of my head. "Can you keep a secret?"

"I guess so. Sure."

"My mother is not going to touch this room because Claudia Montoya-Jones once spent the night here, and it was the most memorable night of my life. So far, that is."

The story of Claudia Montoya-Jones, at least as Mira told it, covered four decades, and it seemed to take that long in the telling. Mr. Lambert's first cousin once removed, Claudia Montoya-Jones was an extra in several movies in the 1920s, and then in the '30s, '40s and '50s she declared herself a spiritual advisor and supported herself by offering a variety of services. Her preferred method for contacting the spirits was deep reverie. She also used tarot cards and a Ouija board, but these she dismissed as mere devices. Props for the uninitiated. As an actress she could not have convinced anyone that she was alive, much less become a character. But as a medium she had a faithful following; there were half a dozen producers who swore they would never make another movie without first consulting her. Vivien Leigh thought she was swell. She was married four times, each time to an older man who died within two years of the wedding. She did all right for herself. She corresponded with Edgar Cayce for six months until his death. And when she herself died in 1964 she was alone, except for her contacts with the spirit world. A short while before her death she visited Mira's father; she ate dinner with the family, told stories about Selznick and Goldwyn, then long after midnight climbed the stairs to the room on the third floor. Mira was eight years old and supposed to be in bed, but she knocked on the door anyway. Madame Claudia showed Mira various mementos that she supposed would interest a child: a lock of Clark Gable's hair; a picture of herself and Orson Welles; a note from Bette Davis.

"I sat at her feet, but I couldn't think of a thing to say that wouldn't sound stupid and childish. I don't know what I had expected. She began to whisper, saying that what she was about to tell me was to be kept in the strictest confidence, that my parents— especially my mother—would be furious with her if they ever found out. She talked about astral projection, the transmigration of souls, Madame Blavatsky, reincarnation, theosophy, immortality. She showed me a necklace of crystals. It was a present to me, she said, but I'd have to wait until she was gone before I could collect it. It would be hidden somewhere in this room, and I'd have to let the crystals call to me. Not five minutes after she left, I was turning the room upside down. The boxsprings of the bed, behind the pictures on the walls, the lampshades. Nothing. I closed my eyes and a little while later I felt an impression of heat coming from the fireplace. That's where I found the necklace, wedged above the door of the flue. She also left me her Ouija board and pointer, which I found in the nightstand next to the bed even though I had checked there once before for the necklace. Whether she meant to leave the Ouija board, I don't know. I couldn't ask my parents. I promised my silence, and I've kept my promise until now. This room is saturated with the soul of Claudia Montoya-Jones, and I refuse to lose her presence just because of some stupid remodeling. My mother doesn't understand. Daddy might, but he'd feel guilty about crossing her."

"See," she said, holding what looked like dime-store jewelry in one hand and a battered box in the other. "You don't believe me."

"I didn't say that." I was yawning, and I couldn't stop. "I told you, I'm tired."

She bit her lip and she seemed about to cry. "I have to show you something tonight. I'll meet you in your room at nine o'clock," she said. "I know that's how you and Freddy get out of the house—your window. I saw you last night. You looked like a couple of apes running across the lawn. But don't worry, I won't say a word to Mom or Dad."

Freddy had warned me that his sister was weird, but I truly wasn't prepared for the degree to which that weirdness might run. I honestly hadn't given it much thought. The night before, after we had made our escape from the house, I followed Freddy through the back gardens and down an overgrown path that crossed the highway before terminating at the river. There were four others waiting for us on the ribbon of sand they called a beach, a small fire already burning. Freddy made the introductions: Duncan Rhodes and Sheila Baird, Sheila's sister Amanda, and Gale Lewis.

"Fish Becker," Freddy said. "He's staying with us this summer."

"I suppose there's a story behind your name," Gale Lewis said. A dark-eyed girl as soft-featured as a pillow, she snuggled up to Freddy. Her lips curved in what I could only think of as a proprietary smile.

"I fell into a pond when I was three," I said, "and I nearly drowned. My father has a sense of humor though; my name is really Calvin or Cal, but I can't ever remember anyone calling me that."

"Poor baby," Sheila said, "that must have been frightening."

"Actually, I don't remember falling into the pond either, so maybe none of it's true except for the name. And the fact that I hate seafood."

I can't say that I remember too much of the evening beyond the preliminaries; two bottles of bourbon, lifted from Duncan Rhodes' parents' liquor cabinet, began to make the rounds, and I took my turn, so some sort of haze seems to cover everything. Sheila and Duncan told the story of how they managed to sneak the bottles out of the house even though Duncan's father was home and drinking from the opened one at the time. It had all been quite a clandestine operation, and they laughed so hard tears squeezed from Sheila's eyes as they told of hearing Duncan's father flailing around his study. "I could hear him turning over chairs," Duncan said. "And he was roaring at my mother: 'Margaret, the goddamn whiskey disappeared again.' I would have preferred gin, but it was worth it to hear the old man go on." Sheila's sister Amanda—who had obviously been brought along as my date for the evening— took an exceptionally large gulp, choked, coughed, then giggled: a light falsetto that ended in an embarrassing snort which the others pretended not to have heard. Not long after the first bottle was finished, Freddy and Gale left to take a walk, and then Sheila and Duncan also stood up, saying they felt the need of some exercise. They staggered a bit getting to their feet, and moments later we heard them moving off into the quack grass. Then there was the sound of a belt buckle and the rustle of clothing, and Amanda began to unbutton her plaid flannel shirt as if she had heard a signal. She had accompanied her sister on outings before.

"You can kiss me and touch me, but nothing further," she said.

"Oh."

In Los Angeles the girls who had consented to go with me to football games or dances had been remarkably aggressive kissers but extremely reticent to abandon any article of clothing; by their conversation one might have imagined them as having night jobs, and yet they always made sure to have breath mints handy and they always kept a sharp watch on the clock and the time when they would go home to their parents and the security of a four-poster bed. So my sexual experience had been limited to that which can be accomplished before curfew and in spite of the impediment of however many layers of clothing.

Amanda was another variation on the theme. She pulled the tails of her shirt out of her jeans. "Well? I'm not doing everything. I said you could kiss me." She took a wad of gum out of her mouth and placed it beside her on the sand, a prim and rather delicate gesture. I had an unsettling vision of her putting it back in her mouth when we had finished for the evening.

She had long, straight brown hair and a wide face, surprisingly pliable lips and a playful tongue. She wore braces, so that was a bit of a danger—one had to be careful or the cuts could be severe and take forever to heal—and I could taste, in addition to the whiskey and the grape gum, onion and garlic and pepperoni. Pizza for dinner, I thought, and no mints for this girl. Her bra was something of a mystery, but she was patient while I struggled, and she used the opportunity while my attentions were elsewhere to suck so hard on my tongue that even a day later it felt as though something had torn.

"So what are you doing at Lamberts'?" she said during a pause in our labors. "Why aren't you at Malibu or Zuma?"

We had been tussling for an hour, and I had discovered certain limits: fondling her small, bare breasts was acceptable, rolling on top of her, my legs between hers, was not; stroking the small of her back made her hum, but when my hand drifted lower, she kneed me, and I was fortunate that her aim was slightly off.

"My parents are in Germany," I said. "They're thinking about getting divorced, and whenever they think about getting divorced, they like to take little trips and spend a lot of money."

"Germany's not a little trip."

"No, that's why I think it might be serious this time."

"Mine have been divorced for two years. Mom's living in an ashram so we stayed with our dad."

"Sorry."

"It's no big deal. They yelled a lot before they split up, so this is better, I think. Not so much crossfire."

Our kissing changed then from the violent imitations of the biting and chewing we had seen on movie screens to something quieter, friendlier.

"There now. This is nice," Amanda said. "Don't you think?"

"Sure." We were pecking away at each other like a couple of birds. It was nice, sure. Delicious, I might have said, to lie next to someone who seemed easy enough to be with. Though I admit I was also wondering how I might relieve her of her jeans and how I could protect myself in the event of discovery.

Amanda kissed me good morning in front of her father's house just as a gray band along the eastern horizon signaled dawn. She squeezed my hand and we promised to meet when the others did, knowing that Freddy and Gale, Duncan and Sheila had already made plans for tonight.

"I had a good time, Fish."

"Me, too."

She carefully opened the screen door, and I waited until she waved to me from her window upstairs, then I drifted uphill toward the Lambert property. I had not wanted to be here originally; in the days after my parents had announced their plans, the word *abandoned* had taken possession of my thoughts like the tune of a commercial that, by its insidious nature, is impossible to shake. And yet the Lamberts had proven to be much more parental than my own mother and father, Freddy was the older brother I had always wanted but never had, Mira was Mira, and Amanda was a welcome bonus. I was dazed by bourbon, the proximity of sex, and the goodness of my good luck, and I would have been happy to curl up in the bushes bordering the Lamberts' house. Freddy, however, was pacing at the bottom of his driveway. "Come on. We're late. The old man finds out, I'll be cutting firewood every night this summer. And you won't be getting any more Amanda pie."

We entered the house the way we had exited, the sun forming an orange corona behind Mount Hood as we stepped through the window to my room. Freddy headed off to the shower—his father had arranged a job for him with a construction crew, and work started early each morning—while I pitched forward onto my bed. Only to discover that I was wide awake. Again. So far, for the ten nights of my stay with the Lamberts, I had slept badly if at all. I would walk upstairs yawning my head off, but the moment my head hit the pillow my brain would begin to churn, as if some poltergeist of my imagination were forcing me to replay the day's events. With Amanda in the picture it wasn't a wholly unwelcome task. *If only I could get some sleep.* I thrashed around in bed, trying to think of all the tricks said to cure insomnia, only to play Hell Bridge with Mira a few hours later and agree to meet her tonight. It would work out okay, I told myself. I would listen to more of Mira's nonsense, then there would be Amanda: a reward for the courtesy. The summer was turning out to be more interesting and more complicated than I would have thought possible. And if I got a little rest, I might be able to enjoy it.

Promptly at nine o'clock that evening, Mira knocked on my door.

"All right, Fish, let's get this show on the road." Clutched across her chest was the box containing the Ouija board, a backpack was slung over one shoulder, and like Amanda the night before, she wore a plaid flannel shirt. Given Mira's preoccupations, the conjunction startled me as though the two girls had somehow exchanged bits of body and soul.

"Okay, fine." I stepped into the hallway to go downstairs, but Mira held up her hand.

"Nope. We go the way you went last night." She pointed toward my window. "That way."

"Why? We can use the stairs and the front door. Who cares if we go out now?"

"That way." She was adamant.

"I just followed Freddy. I didn't even look where we were going, I was that scared. We could fall off the roof."

"I trust you."

"I wouldn't," I said. "I don't trust me."

"Chicken."

"You can say that again."

"Chicken, chicken, chicken." And then she started making *buck, buck* chicken noises, which seemed like a pretty cheap trick for a serious theosophist. Shouldn't she have been able to summon the spirit of Claudia Montoya-Jones or whoever to fly her out the window? She was not to be denied, however, and soon enough I stepped out the window. The sun was not yet completely set, so seeing my way was not the problem; my fear of heights, which had not been engaged during the darkness of the night before, was. The slate tiles of the roof threatened to spin under my feet.

"Come on, Fish." Mira pushed me in the back. "Let's go. You've got a date with Amanda Baird at midnight, right? You wouldn't want to miss that."

How she knew that, I couldn't be sure. The likeliest explanation was that earlier this evening she had talked with her brother, but the thought also occurred to me that she had talked with some spirit or other and that was the source of her information. An idea like that threatened to send me off the edge as literally as her fingers in my back.

"Don't push. I'm doing the best that I can."

"Let's go then."

She had things to show me, she said. We managed our way off the roof and down the trellis, then onto a path that led us away from the river. The path climbed a slight rise through a stand of fir and cedar that abruptly ended after less than one hundred yards. The slight incline also fell away with equal abruptness into a smooth slope broken only by the angular shapes of granite monuments, grave markers and private mausoleums. Some of the older stones sported likenesses of the deceased or the comfort and consolation of angels. One of the largest mausoleums, a replica of the Parthenon, suggested that the tenants had progressed to that state of divine wisdom to which we all aspire. As dusk became more profound, the view afforded this community of the dead became more remarkable as well: the dark curve of the river acquired a greater density in the foreground while the lights of the city's east side glittered within its basin made of hills.

"Yes," I said, "it's pretty. No question."

"Maybe so, but it's not what we came here for."

"Oh?"

I followed her down an asphalt walkway that curved around another wall of fir trees into an outlying section of the cemetery, its suburbs if you will. Here the plots were indicated by brass markers, and the grassy field stretched away in a uniform barrenness. Only a few pots of plastic flowers provided occasional relief. At the bottom of the hill within a chain link enclosure stood an aluminum storage shed and next to that was a backhoe silhouetted in the gathering darkness. And not far from the backhoe were the tarp-draped mounds of dirt from a recently dug hole.

"Here we are," Mira said. She put down the box with her Ouija board, then fished around in her backpack, coming up with a flashlight which she first aimed into the earth then handed to me. "See anything?"

"No. Should I?"

She shrugged, pulled out a hammer and a rope ladder from the pack, and began to pound two tent stakes into the grass at the lip of the grave, hooking the loops at the top of the ladder around the stakes when she was finished. "Down we go."

"This is stupid," I said. Still my foot was on the second rung of the ladder. "You really are weird, Mira. You know that?"

She nodded absently. "I don't mind so much." She wedged the flashlight into the wall of soft dirt so its light fanned between us. "Have a seat."

Sitting cross-legged, we faced one another and placed the Ouija board on our knees. Claudia Montoya-Jones had been convinced, Mira said, that the dead were not really dead, merely in another dimension. Cemeteries were reminders that these two dimensions were no more remote from one another than two rooms which are connected by a single doorway. One can have a foot in both if one is willing to stand on the threshold. A person of such heightened awareness as Claudia Montoya-Jones could stand on that threshold while she was rinsing out her underwear; Mira felt that as a novice she stood a better chance of success if she was located in the physical actuality of the grave, as well as its symbolic sensibility.

David Borofka

"Close your eyes," Mira said. "Be still. This may take a bit."

"Not too long, or I may fall asleep." I yawned with a certain measure of exaggeration. I meant it as a joke, but right then, the same trouble that had afflicted my last ten nights took command. What was I doing here? Sitting in a grave with a girl who was, if not certifiably crazy, then at least off-center by a goodly margin. The ground on the floor of the grave was relatively soft, yet even so I seemed to have found the one hard lump to sit on, and try as I might I couldn't find any relief. Did cemeteries have night watchmen? Would our being here constitute some sort of desecration? Certainly it would be a social faux pas, if not a moral error, to be convicted of trespassing in a graveyard. My father would surely find it as amusing as any fraternity prank. He told his own stories of youthful indiscretions. He had once attached a drooping plaster-of-Paris cock to the reproduction of Rodin's Thinker that stood watch over the library. He had loads of such stories. But would his own amusement last if he were told he needed to wire money for my bail?

"Spirits, are you here with us?"

Mira's voice broke through my own reverie, and I felt the pointer move underneath my fingers, faster than I could have attributed to my own unconscious desire to be shocked. The pointer slid to the word Yes and stopped.

"Madame Claudia, please address us, if you can."

The pointer moved away from Yes, then returned, again with a rapidity I found unsettling.

"Madame Claudia, we have with us tonight a doubter—"

"I never said that."

"—a doubter, who needs to be convinced of the reality of the immortal dimension. He will ask a question that only he knows the answer to. Your answer will be his answer regarding the truth of your existence. Fish?"

"I don't know what to say."

"Ask a question. Madame Claudia is waiting."

"What am I supposed to ask?"

"Anything." She was becoming impatient with me now. "Just ask a question."

"Fine. What's the capital of California?"

"No, no, no," Mira said, "not that kind of question. Everyone knows that. You have to ask something that no one else knows about."

"This is stupid."

"Just do it, Fish."

"All right, let's play your stupid game. What does my father think of Mira's father? There, that's my question."

I expected Mira to move the pointer to a predictable answer, one that would spell out F-R-I-E-N-D, but instead it moved to three letters then stopped.

"S-0-B," Mira spelled, her confusion so obvious that her forehead was creased in concentration. "Sob. What does that mean?"

"Nothing. I told you this was stupid. I've had enough. Look," I said, standing up and upsetting the board and pointer, "this is an idiotic game and you're as nuts as they come."

I climbed the rope ladder as fast as I could go, and I thought seriously of throwing it down into the hole, give Mira a dose of her own symbolic sensibilities, as it were. I could hear Mira calling to me from the grave, her voice muffled by the damp earth. But instead of waiting for her I began to jog back toward the older part of the cemetery, certain that an evening of exercise with Amanda could make up for the past hour. As I neared the crest of the hill, the markers and monuments again became more elaborate, the sentiments on each stone more roundly effusive of the departed one's value to family and friends. Small landscape lights indicated the turns and intersections of various paths, but in the darkness I missed the landmarks I had remembered from an hour before—an angel here, a temple there—and I lost my way. I did not slow down, however, until the dark figure of a man holding a rifle rose up before me.

"Don't shoot," I cried, throwing up my hands. "I'm lost. I didn't mean to be here."

This was in the center of the cemetery, and I soon realized that I was pleading with a memorial for a veteran of World War I. Sweat trickled down my neck and back, and as I crouched next to the puttees of this dead soldier of the Great War, I shivered in the cool evening air.

My father maintained that Miles Lambert was "the luckiest son of a bitch on the face of God's green earth." This assessment was probably three-quarters envy and one-quarter admiration since Miles Lambert's material success was in no small part fueled by his marriage and his wife's inherited wealth. And it seemed obvious that it was to this judgment that the Ouija board had referred. "I've done well with what I was given," my father liked to say, "but Miles stumbled onto the mother lode and he still hasn't figured out what he's got."

It was a curious kind of sentiment from my father, who normally was blind to class distinctions, but in this case, as someone from a lower economic stratum, he was all too uncomfortably aware that someone his own age, a childhood pal no less, was so much more prosperous. It further galled him that Mr. Lambert did not seem to care all that much about the ornaments of affluence, but instead preferred to tinker with the old radios that sat on shelves lining the basement walls. His wife had a gold mine of old family stocks such as Coca-Cola, IBM, and GM, but he had had the foresight to diversify into real estate, and it was rumored, my father said, that he had owned at one time or another half of Portland's downtown. Whether that information was correct or not, I never knew, but I did know that Miles Lambert was totally unaffected by prosperity. He drove a twenty-year-old Buick, his clothes were seldom fancy, jeans and tee shirts the rule, and he derived more satisfaction from a well-played point in squash than the closing of a multi-million-dollar land deal. My father, who was no piker himself when it came to making money, was baffled by such attitudes, since between his own impulses and my mother's, they were usually teetering on the edge of some new precipice of insolvency. Any proof of extra liquidity fascinated my father, who seldom carried enough cash to pay for parking.

I say all this because, although my father would not have acknowledged it, I believe he hoped that my spending the summer with the Lamberts might rub off on me as well as our family. Maybe the luck that had followed the Lamberts for the last twenty years would follow me home and rescue the Beckers from further fiscal misfortunes. And maybe my exposure to the Lamberts would also put me on a more definite course of maturation. I was, frankly, a disappointment to my father; he could not resist comparing me to Freddy, who was already over six feet tall and, from acting as his father's squash partner, full of rude animal health. When my father looked at me he saw what I saw in the mirror every morning: a shapeless, unformed human being, masculine in gender, but wholly lacking in what he considered the male gifts—charm and good manners, a distinct understanding of one's vocational calling, and maybe most important, athletic prowess in the recreational activities of the elite such as squash, tennis and golf. Instead, I had a tendency to wipe my nose with my sleeve, I was a lackadaisical student who did not have a clue—or a care—about my future, and as far as sports were concerned I was as deft as a pile of sand.

So went my thinking while I sat at the base of that long-forgotten soldier, under the gun so to speak, all precipitated by Mira's Ouija board. Madame Claudia had gotten to the heart of things; my father, as much as he loved Miles Lambert out of respect for their shared pasts, thought of him as a son of a bitch, a lucky one. But so much worse was the realization of what my father felt about me: I had known it for quite some time—maybe years—but had never before admitted to myself in that way of honesty that, when it strikes, has the force of a cathartic.

Mira found me finally, the beam of her flashlight cutting a swathe across the grass, the stones, the legs of the soldier, my face. And then she showed me a shortcut home, another path that ran along the north side of the house, entering the grounds by the swimming pool. Rarely used anymore, the pool, built in the 1920s, had been the scene of many a party. Now, however, the tiles were chipped and stained, the concrete pitted, the water a brackish green. The wrought-iron ladders on either side were Art Deco monstrosities: Beardsley women rising from the depths of their murky sea; in the beam of the flashlight the ladders went down into the green water for three inches and disappeared.

"Who's for a swim?" Mira said.

"No thanks, not me. I have a date, remember?"

"With Amanda. How could I forget? Come on, you've got oodles of time."

She snapped the light off, and in two quick movements she had shucked her shoes and jeans and glasses and plunged into the water, swimming the length of the pool in one breath. When she called again, her voice came from the far end. "Come on in, Fish, the water's fine."

"Not me. I'm going to the house." Through the trees, I could see the windows glowing gold, doorways between darknesses. Somewhere down the hill a car started, a radio blared. "Did you hear me, Mira? I'm going."

Silence. A small sound, less a splash, a ripple maybe. Mira swimming underwater?

"I'm going. Mira?"

Still no response. I felt along the tiles for the flashlight, switched it on, and let the light play along the surface. No Mira.

"Oh, God. Oh, Christ," I said. "Mira." If she was really underwater and in trouble there was no way to see her, no way to know. How would I explain it to Mr. and Mrs. Lambert when they saw the bloated body of their daughter, green water streaming from her hair, eyes, nose, and mouth? How could I face them if I hadn't tried to help?

I was unlacing my shoes when the push came from behind. There are those moments in cartoons when the branch falls, the cliff crumbles, and the character is left suspended in the air, realization of the drop to come just beginning to dawn. I went sailing, and the water took forever in rising to greet me. The air seemed to be a conduit of memory, and the words *so this is how you are born* came of their own accord. Then came the water and a darkness ten times more opaque than the night. I swam to where I thought a ladder should be, but before Mira could find me with the beam of the flashlight, I went headfirst into one of the Beardsley ladies. Blood ran into my eyes, and the world, already dark, lost focus as well. I hung onto the ladder with one hand and stanched my wound with the other. Mira stood over me, dripping, in her panties and the flannel shirt, the flashlight waving in her hand. As she saw my face her eyes widened myopically, unaccustomed to vision without the aid of lenses.

"Jeez Louise, you're bleeding."

"You didn't have to push me, you know."

"We've got bandages upstairs."

We trudged up to the house. My clothes were streaming, my shoes, which I never had a chance to remove, were squashy, and I was covered with slime. When I suggested that we go in the front door like normal folk, Mira nodded her agreement, and though we wiped our feet we left a trail of wet footprints behind.

She bandaged my forehead in her room. I lay on the braided rug while she applied Mercurochrome and gauze. Her lips were pursed. "I probably ought to get my mother. You might need stitches."

"It's fine," I said, yawning suddenly, "It's just a cut."

"And you've got a date tonight."

"And I've got a date."

Through her opened windows came the intimations of yet another summer night. Crickets chirruping near the reflecting pool. The smell of lighter fluid and charcoal burning. The flat white disk of the moon suddenly swimming into view.

"Did you know," Mira said, "that ten years ago when your parents came to visit, our fathers had a fight in the gazebo?"

"Who told you that? Claudia Montoya-Jones?"

She looked surprised at the suggestion. "No, my mother told me. They were drinking Bloody Marys and watching the sunrise. Our mothers went inside the house to check on the three of us and to scramble some eggs, and by the time they came back outside, our fathers were flailing away at each other. They had just come back from a squash game, so they had their racquets with them in the gazebo. Your father broke a bamboo Slazenger over Daddy's head and drew blood, and that ended the fight, but they never said what started it."

"Probably a let point," I said. "My father hates let points. Last winter he threw his racquet into the balcony after one."

Mira had other ideas about the fight, most of which had to do with the souls of our fathers, and when Mira got going on the subject of soul and theosophical perspective, there was no stopping her. No doubt Madame Claudia had been busy filling her in on all the juicy tidbits. Their struggle was the struggle of two souls imprisoned too long in corrupted flesh. Our fathers were too concerned with the material rather than the spiritual, and so on and so on.

I didn't make it to the conclusion. Sleep—deeper than any I've ever known, before or since, an enchantment of sleep—at last found me. I remember nothing, not a change of positions, not a moment's wakefulness; I may have experienced the impossibility of a night without dreaming. When I woke, sunshine was streaming through Mira's opened windows and dust motes twirled in the air like fireflies. Mira was not in the room, her bed had not been slept in. I was alone. I woke with the thought that Amanda would be waiting, that I needed to hurry to the river, that I was only seven or eight hours late. And then I realized just how absurd a notion that was.

Outside, Mr. Lambert was using a long pole with a net on the end to skim leaves and the occasional frog from the reflecting pool. The frogs were frantic in the net, jumping to escape their rescue; upon their release, they bounced into the grass then made for the bushes like a shot.

I stood away from the window and watched from the shadows. I wasn't about to lean on the casement and declare myself. There were too many things I couldn't fathom. Whether my parents loved either me or each other. Why their millionaire friend would do his own yardwork, clean his own pool, and look happy in the process. I couldn't imagine my parents and the Lamberts young.

David Borofka

The sky was a deep blue, and the few high clouds could not disguise the mountain or hide the sun; in the reflecting pool was an image of land and sky, broken only by the raising and lowering of the dripping, wriggling net and the tracery of an occasional breeze.

David Borofka is a past winner of *The Missouri Review* Editors' Prize contest.

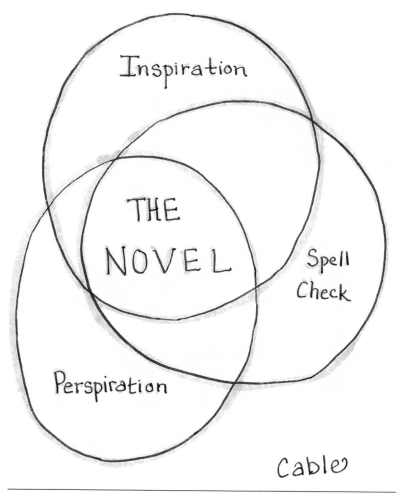

GRIEF / *Marilyn Hacker*

for Iva

I

You turned twenty, and your best friend died
a week after your birthday, in a car
on a bright icy morning. Now you are
flying home. I called; you called back. You howled;
   you cried
like the child you probably ceased to be
the moment that I told you she was dead—
your anchor, homegirl, unsolicited
sister.
      Now you are standing in front of me,
tall and in tears and I have nothing to say.
You're too big for me to hold in my skinny arms,
but I do, windbreaker, backpack and all,
stroke snow-splotched hair you probably chewed
   in a storm
of tears in the cab. Your garment bag leans on the wall,
a black dress in it.
          Now I am watching you growing away
from me, towards hours in a car you and two
   friends drive
through the same treacherous snow, to empty her dorm
room, to sit with the injured boy, wired and re-formed
in plaster, weeping because he was still alive;
toward where you never would have expected to come
and see your friend, or what briefly remained of
   your friend
thin and naked under a sheet, the wound
at her temple inconsequential-looking (a slight
line of dried blood from her ear), stopped still
   on a white
marble slab in a crematorium.

II

Your great-aunts, centenarian-and-some,
give interviews. Stroke-silenced, your grandmother

turned eighty in a Brooklyn nursing home,
looking as if she might stand up, recover
her thoughts, her coat, and walk off toward the L
train—though she won't. Chemo has let me live
so far. Some fluke, prudence, or miracle
has kept your father seronegative.
The January day they called you out
of computer lab so you could phone
home, I'm sure you mentally ran down
your list of possible mortalities,
guessing that it was death it was about,
assuming that it would be one of these.

III

Your "black dress" was the velvet skirt you wear
for choir recitals. K.J., who stood behind
you at the door, her coat still on, her hands
empty and open, met you at the air-
port, since I was sick. Your grief came in-
doors like another illness, one which we
could hardly palliate with soup and tea,
which didn't stop me from making tea again
when I could let you go.
        But you had gone
farther away, to where she was a light
receding as you watched, to where she was
teasing you on the train, to Argelès
to where she left you at the bus stop ten
days past, to where she glaringly was not.

IV

I booked you three at the Hotel Malher
—sixth floor, no bath, a hundred-fifty francs.
You crowded on my couch, made phone calls, drank
tea, took turns showering and washing hair.
You'd had breakfast. You'd gone to the bank.
You all were seventeen. A girl in Tours,
her pen pal, had invited you to come
down for the weekend. You would take the train.
And then you'd take the train to Perpignan.
Was there a train from Tours to Perpignan?
Her mother's (gay) friend had a summer home

in Argelès, had offered the spare room.
(I think I had to route you through Bordeaux.)
You were blasé, from years I'd ferried you
over, "Unaccompanied," to France.
She'd spent six exchange months in Budapest,
could be acute about the difference,
but mostly loved the light, the river, under
the influence. The boy seemed youngest,
and anything *she* liked, except museums,
he was willing to attest was wonder-
ful too. Like colts, like April trees, your threesome
bristled with innocence and confidence.
A sprained ankle, lost camera, missed train
were the mishaps that you thought to fear.
I sent you out into the summer rain
between your junior and your senior year.

V

A crowd, standing-room-only, turned out for
her funeral. Masses of wasted flowers
embraced a photo album you'd spent hours
assembling, through the night and dawn, with her
shell-shocked kid sister. Then you'd gone together
to face your first cadaver, and belief
in the obscenity that caused your grief.
The obsequies of a dead senator
might not have brought out such a throng, I said,
standing in line waiting my turn to view
family snapshots: mother and infant, two
year old walking, standing on her head
at eight—domestic Sunday afternoon
pastime turned into mourning. She herself
was now a box of ashes on a shelf
whose sixteen-year-old shadow mugged at you
next to a Beatles poster in your blue
disheveled bedroom while you took that one.

Marilyn Hacker is the author of eight books, including *Selected Poems 1965-1990* and *Winter Numbers*.

THE GIRL'S BOOK OF MATH/ *Leslie Daniels*

WILDGIRL'S ADVICE ON HOW TO HEAL A BROKEN HEART:

D ANCE A LOT.
Do anything that involves music so long as it doesn't involve musicians.

Think of a rude name for your ex. How about Roughtrade?

Think of borrowing fifty dollars from your roommate and offering it to your ex to let you piss on him. He needs the money.

Your ex is in your body still so lose weight, almost every American can. Stop eating. You'll be one of those girls, those spare lines that own the city. The lines say to hell with food, to hell with eating, give me sex and art. Give me a cigarette. Touch me in a public place. Rub your knuckle between the legs of my jeans, there's lots of space.

Laugh till you cry. Cry till you laugh. Get a motto.

Send your ex an unsigned two-hundred-dollar check and this note: *I know you are having money troubles. I would sign this if you let me urinate on you. As ever,*

Try these mottos:
Go fast till it gets good, then slow down.
Life is a drug, so boot it.

Don't fall in love again yet, wait till you forget your ex's phone number, or six weeks, whichever comes first.

Don't go to a therapist. Remember, you are vulnerable now and it's a bad time to get help, you could really get to depend on it.

Think about if your uncle would lend you money, maybe five hundred dollars. Tell your uncle it's for rent. It is, you want to rent your ex for a degrading act.

More mottos:
Motion is everything.
Avoid sentiment.
Seek beauty in ugliness, at least nobody will bother you.

Don't go to the movies. Movies try to sell you a shiny, stupid life. You have a life.

Realize one day you don't want to piss on him, you want to want to piss on him. Call that Health.

"For thirty-two cents, a man in a blue uniform will not carry six inches of slightly soiled lace seven miles, but for forty-two cents he will," said Tina. She dropped a pair of pink underpants into a shoebox. The panties had been an early love token to Jerry, who returned them in an envelope that arrived marked "insufficient postage." Her roommate, Everardo, had given the postman a dime.

The shoebox contained four mugs with TINA on them, several very large tee shirts and a pile of letters from Jerry that she had been trying to read to Everardo all morning. Ev was smoking a half-joint from the night before and sipping espresso from a tiny blue cup. He had suggested Tina clean house to help her over her broken heart. At least get rid of Jerry's old tee shirts, he said, I can smell them from the sidewalk.

Ev believed in cleaning and ironing. He believed the world had only two kinds of people in it, the ones who made their beds and the others. Tina's bed was a loft in the room where they kept all their clothes. When he worked, Ev was a stylist for fashion shoots. When he slept home, it was on the couch in the living room. They called the couch "she," as in, "I'll sleep on her tonight." Since Jerry had dumped Tina, they never said "he" at all, everything male or just plain had become she.

I have a wife, Jerry had told Tina last weekend, like he had just remembered it. Where? Tina wanted to know. Kutztown, I'm going back there. What? Tina said and she kept saying it for a week.

It had been a long week. Tina spent a lot of it crying in the biology lab of the University of Pennsylvania where she worked. Her eyes stayed puffy. They went from morning pale and puffy to late afternoon red and puffy. Everardo was trying to help her rally. On the bathroom door he had drawn a chart. The X axis was time, and the Y axis was missing Jerry. "Look," he said, "the line goes down. Here's Monday up here and Friday way down here."

"Asymptotic," Tina had sniffed, "it'll never be a zero." Tina had been a math whiz once. When she was seven she had invented negative numbers. But then she found out that someone else had gotten there first, which counts in math the way it does in sex and mountains. It didn't count then to Tina. At seven, she had felt a high, clear buzzing in her brain as if a huge beam was shining through it and out her eyes and fingertips. If she had thought about herself she would have said, I feel brilliant. But she didn't. She thought about numbers then, and what numbers could

Leslie Daniels

do. She thought of them with affection. She thought of them as having shapes. She marveled at how threes and twos looked like themselves, and above all at what nines could do, how a nine could leave its print on any number. How the nine times tables inverted themselves. How her sister was nine. How big that was. Nine. Tina had been looking for magic, real magic, for a long time, and she thought that in nines she had finally found it.

Now she rarely talked numbers except with Ev. He had started it. "Everything is four," Ev said once. "'Cat,' say, is three letters. 'Three' is five letters. 'Five,' four letters. Everything is four, try it."

Tina did. It took her back to before she left math, before boys arrived and math became less interesting. "'Everything' is ten. 'Ten' is three. 'Three' is five. 'Five' is four. Amazing." And then, "Boys must grow into numbers, girls grow out of them."

"Wanna hear one, Ev?" Tina said, unfolding a letter from the shoebox. "Just one little love note?" Ev said nothing. He was stroking Herbst the dog, who rarely tolerated touch. "Dear Tina, I miss the inside of your arm, the little corner where the bruise comes when the nurse draws blood. I want to kiss you there."

"Makes me want to puke like a bad girl," Ev said.

"He said sweet stuff to me, Ev. He said making love with me was like driving a Cadillac."

"Off the lot?" Ev widened his huge dark eyes. They were set at the edges of his face. His hair was cut close to his narrow head, the same width as his long neck. He had a dancer's wide shoulders and descending from them, a liquid black body. His hands were small and the fingers stubby. He wore cheap, exquisite shoes.

Herbst got up and stared at a spot between his nose and the fake mantelpiece. He suffered from dog flashbacks. Ev had adopted Herbst from the Retired Greyhound Placement Program in Saratoga Springs, and the dog still ran in circles rather than lines. He never looked directly at anyone except Josephine, their cat, who had not been seen in a week. Their apartment in a rough part of Philadelphia was surrounded by fighting, and Josephine made the most of it. She only came back when she was too sore to scrap anymore and then slept for a day or so. Everardo had the worst time in the neighborhood. Guys called "Yo, homo" to him and he answered "Pardon me," since that's how they talked in Ardmore, where he grew up. Tina, being white, was mostly ignored.

"I can't stand the idea that he gets over me at a faster rate than I get over him," she said. Ev took a deep drag on the joint. Herbst propped his paws on the fake mantelpiece where the laminated playing cards were displayed ("Great Women of Science"—Madame Curie was the ace and Margaret Mead the ten). Herbst sniffed them.

"Wildgirl says I need a motto. I met her at Old City Coffee last night while you were clubbing. How about 'It ain't over till the fat lady sings'?"

"Tina, the fat lady did Aïda." Josephine, true to form, appeared from nowhere and walked up the long ramp of Ev's body, one ear folded down.

"Benjamin Franklin says," Ev put his choir-boy voice on, "Benjamin Franklin says, 'Measure your health by your sympathy with morning.'" He giggled. Josephine stepped off his chest and onto the kitchen table where she lay on top of Wildgirl's "HEAL A BROKEN HEART" instruction page.

Wildgirl was the closest Tina had to a girlfriend. She had introduced Tina to Jerry, who worked with her at Old City Coffee, and now she felt as near to guilt as Wildgirl could feel, which was mad. "I wrote this for you," she had said the night before when she handed Tina the xeroxed page, across the little table without knee room. "Love is a dangerous thing, look at Everardo and Jaime. Jaime OD'd after he got sick because he loved Ev and he knew he'd given it to him."

"Does Ev have it?"

Wildgirl sighed and flapped her long square knees open under her flowered dress. Wildgirl never wore underpants, she said they were part of a drug-company plot. "Don't *you* know?"

"Ev doesn't talk about himself."

"You should ask. You're probably too busy with your *feelings*." She sang this last word. Tina had just described to her how at this very barrel table, last Saturday, Jerry had told her about his wife, and how Tina felt the heavy hollowness of her heartbreak. You only met him in March, Wildgirl said. But Tina told her it had been a whole time, with a beginning and a middle. She couldn't say "end," she was living out the end part still.

"It was terrible with Jaime." Wildgirl drew in the spilled milk foam. "I didn't know pills were messy. And the cops were the worst part, so rude. In their rubber suits. They left the bloody suits in Jaime and Ev's hallway. Pasty bastards."

"I didn't know about Ev. It may not be, you know, certain. It's not always transmitted." She put some money down for her latte, which Wildgirl pocketed. "Thanks for the poem. I have to walk Herbst, Ev is out, I should go."

Ev hadn't come home before Tina went to bed, and she'd found him this morning, dressed in his club clothes in the same kitchen chair where he was still sitting now.

"Ev, I've cleaned up, anyway this box is full. Let's take Herbst to the park and let her run."

"I can't go out, I'm not high enough yet." The phone rang and Ev slid down the chair, perfectly rigid. Tina met him on the floor under the table and they listened to the machine pick up.

Jerry's voice came in, "Yeah, hi Tina, it's Jerry. I just wondered if I could get those shirts back from you. I'll be..."

"R-E-S-P-E-C-T!" Ev shouted, "just a little respect."

"Just a little bit," Tina joined in. She jumped up dancing, her breasts bobbing. Herbst chased where his tail used to be. They drowned out the beep and whir of the machine resetting.

"Tina, wear the green to the park, be a Martian lady."

"OK, then I have to do a hundred sit-ups right now and a hundred butt things." She twisted, looking in the mirror at her backside.

"Marilyn had a big butt."

"And she died."

"You should feature it," Ev said. "You have a great girl ass. One of the all-time finest. Feature it."

"It's a double feature already."

"I'll dress it. Put these on." He handed her a pair of green snakeskin tights he had hand-dyed in the bathtub. Ev had been kicked out of all the neighborhood laundromats for dying clothes in the washers.

She slid into them under her nightshirt. Ev was right, they featured each cheek, high and round. "I don't know. It makes me uncomfortable."

"You just hate the idea of giving anything away for free. It makes your butt look like Amelia Earhart."

"Let's do a Ching to see if we should go to the park or not."

"It furthers one to cross the great ghetto. We'll go to Rittenhouse Square and get a chocolate croissant on the way. You carry Josie and I'll walk Herbst."

They left, the slender black man in black jeans and a black linen shirt, tiny olive-white Tina with her round bottom, the gray dog trailed by the pewter-colored cat.

"I'm hungry like a fat girl," Ev said. They turned onto Latimer Street.

"Ev, why couldn't Jerry just keep loving me? Why did he have to love me and then not love me? I feel like he found out the truth. He found out about the real me that's lazy and mean and selfish."

"Tina, don't do this to yourself. Sometimes I just hate girls."

"I want to call him, Ev. I have his shirts. Should I wash them first? Is it rude to give them back dirty?"

"Burn them, Tina."

"Ev, I miss him."

"You miss being adored, that's all you miss."

"And cock, I miss her too."

Ev laughed and patted Herbst's head.

"Come on then, chocolate cures that." They were at the door of The Commissary.

Tina pulled a five out of her shoe. "Get me two, please."

"I certainly will not."

She waited with the animals on the curb, counting the comments her bottom drew. Four and Ev was back with the pastries.

In Rittenhouse Square, they sat on a bench and watched Herbst chase a circle around Josie, then the fountain, stopping suddenly to stare at the azaleas.

"Ev, we should make something of ourselves."

"We have, this is it."

"Something useful."

"Tina, I may move in with Umberto."

"Oh," she inhaled. "He's that nurse?"

"I'd like to take Josie and Herbst if I could, but I don't want to leave you all alone."

"No, that's ok. Probably better for me not to have the responsibility." She smoothed her palms down her green tights. "What the hell will I wear?"

"I'll do you a clothes chart. And just stay out of The Gap. No catalogues either. I think I need to be with boys. You need to be with boys, too."

"One is a prime number."

Ev took the last bite of his croissant. "Why is it when you start a diet, you instantly look thinner?"

"That's the function of the curve. One point, that one instant describes its whole direction." After a moment, "I'll miss you."

"You'll still see me, silly."

"It's sad isn't it, these times we live in. I've had four relationships and each one ended, like the person died or something."

"They didn't die."

"You're right. But I never got to hold them again. Really, I just want boys for their skin. They talk, I talk, we laugh, but I just want their skin."

Herbst was staring panic-stricken at nothing. Josephine purred, she saw it too.

"If you want to keep them you can."

"No, they'll have a better life with you. I can't really even take care of that sweet potato vine in the jelly jar." They sat on the bench quietly and got panhandled by seven people in a row, each one more anguished looking than the one before.

"Jesus, let's get out of here before Snow White shows up," Ev said.

On their block it was nearly dark.

"Chocolate croissant. How much do I have to bike tomorrow?"

"Six miles, just the Front Street loop. I think you should move in with Martha and Bea."

"Not lesbians, I'll get a reputation. Jerry said he thought I was gay."

"Jerry said dumb stuff to you and you just taped it all on that little Sony Thinkman in your brain."

"Ev, if I'm forty and I still don't have a baby, do you think I could have Jerry impregnate me?"

"Listen to me, Teeny, when you're forty, you won't even remember what he looked like. He'll be a Nehru jacket."

"Madras plaid. Will you still love me?"

"Honey, I'll be in Heaven with the Big Girl."

"Oh God. Oh shit."

"Sha, Teeny. Sha-sha." He kissed the top of her head. Tina put her arms tight around him.

EVERARDO'S RULES FOR DRESSING

1. Do it in the evening, dressing is an entirely evening thing. For mornings, God invented uniforms.
2. If it reminds you of your mother, take it off.
3. If it reminds you of anyone else's mother, take it off.
4. If it wasn't originally a garment, but say a curtain or something for the bath, leave it in the linen closet.
5. Black and white can't be beat.

6. Except by black.
7. If it makes you think of sex acts, don't worry, thinking isn't a crime.
8. Don't invent styles. That's a tall woman's job.
9. If it hurts carry band-aids.
10. When in doubt throw it out.
11. Don't trust women on clothes.
12. Don't trust women on clothes.
13. Press it, you lazy thing.

Leslie Daniels has also published stories in *The Louisville Review* and elsewhere.

WATERTABLES/ *Adam Marshall Johnson*

G ET ME A WITNESS," he yells from downstairs. I'm lying on top of the covers because Molly, god, she's an oven. She sleeps so hot it makes her look unhappy to sleep, pouty, with her skin puffy and red, mouth folded open against the pillow. "Go put him to bed," she says. "Lock his window. It's cool out." Cool, I think. It's July. Her eyes are closed. Her lips move against the pillow. Then she's quiet all over. I've a few more minutes till she's roused again. I stare at the ceiling, at the roof, and listen to the clamor of a hot South Dakota night beneath me. I don't like to see him at night. He gets confused at night. I listen to him rumble around, hear the floorboards under his feet and the soft thuds as he bumps into things. Something crashes below. Mol kicks me through the sheets. "Jim," she mumbles and pauses. Her hair sticks to her damp cheek. I think she's done, but then she adds, "go talk to him." But she's not really awake.

"He's not doing it again," I say. "He's just having a bad dream." I look to see if she'll answer but she just moans some, from the heat. I get up and cross the warm floor to the window and hear her roll up into the free covers on instinct. I look out. My face is in that layer of air that hangs just off the glass and I think it should be cool, I imagine I can see my breath in the pane. It looks like mist out there, looming above the fields, glowing in all the lights. But it's not. It's the dust of topsoil, earth once washed into the Missouri River valley, silt, loam, now leaving us, moving on in a light breeze. We need rain.

I stare into the bean fields and find myself almost looking for her, almost wondering what my father sees, a woman running the plow rows in a blue paper dress. I follow this corridor of dark green as it leads south to the Watertables State Mental Health Facility. It's bigger at night, too big, with the lights always on, shining through the tall hedge that hides the high fence. There's no one out there. She's not out there. I know it.

When I get downstairs I see a racquetball rolled up against the front door. He's yelling in his room, "She's here. She's here." Then I hear him whispering. The hall closet door is open and the light is on. My gear is lying on the floor, racquets, gloves, balls.

He sticks his head into the hall. "She's back," he says. "She came back." And he's gone again, whispering.

In his room, I walk to his bedpost and feel for the string that's run to the overhead light. I rigged it that way so he won't have to get out of bed in the dark, so he won't fall. I chink on the light and we stand there squinting, me and my dad in our underwear. The bedcovers are on the floor. He has dreamed himself out of bed again and he is worked up. He walks to the open window saying, "See." His white hair is standing up straight, unsure of its once-worn part. I pull up his sagging briefs and then shut the window. "Dad, where's the sports bag?"

"I give it to her," he says pointing out the window, looking through the glass to the lights of Watertables across the field. "She said she needed it to carry her stuff. She's running away."

"Stop it, Dad," I say. "There's no lady. We've talked about this. You had a dream. You sleepwalked again. Just show me where the bag is and let's go to bed." Last week it was the silverware. I heard a jangle in the night and in the morning all the forks were gone. "The bag," I say. He looks around the room with me, like he forgot he claims to have given it away. His shorts are slipping down again. I latch the window and try not to look into the dark, try not to encourage him. He thinks maybe I saw her and smiles. "We had a deal," I say. "You agreed to stop doing this. Now where did you hide my bag?"

"She come out of the beanfield," he says talking fast. His lips are pasty from sleep and they stick together as he talks. I bend to look under the bed. "She says they put her in there after her husband died. It's awful in there." He points again out the window.

He must have been looking for something in his sleep. He got confused maybe. He dumped the bag out and then couldn't get everything back in. So he hid the bag. It's hidden here somewhere. I turn to look in the hall again. My useless things are spread all over the floor, bright in hall lights. There are no racquetball courts in South Dakota. I start shuffling the remnants back into the closet with my foot. "Get back into bed, Dad," I yell toward his bedroom. "She's just a dream."

"Her name is Margaret," he says. I stop. I walk into his room. I walk right up to him. "What?"

"She said her name is Margaret."

"There's no Margaret, Dad. There's no ghosts and no escapees and no lady in the beans and she doesn't have a name." I try to slow myself but I'm scaring him. "Tell me she doesn't have a name. Tell me you're making it up. . . . Say it!" But it's night. He gets confused at night.

They're both up before me. I come downstairs to Molly listening to the crop reports and drinking coffee with two hands. She's mad again. Her eyes look swollen, like she's been exercising, sweating, in the sun. She feigns interest in July hogs. The AM radio is one thing Dad wouldn't sacrifice for new tenants. It's on all day. She sets the cup down and begins eating eggs with a spoon. That's all we have now, knives and spoons. "You wore that tie yesterday," she says and twists open a jar of instant.

I take the kettle from the kitchen and fill our cups. We all drink instant now. "You two had quite a night," she says, blowing on her coffee. "He doesn't deserve that, you know." See, she's mad. Molly watches him during the day. She makes glossaries for schoolbooks on the computer. But he's fine during the day. It happens at night, when it's my turn.

I undo my tie; it's reversible, brown and blue, and I look around the room for him. It's not good to talk about this around him.

"He walked to the road for the paper."

"He's doing this on purpose," I say sharply. "He's making it up. When we make him understand he's not going in there, this will all stop." I don't like talking to her this way, but she doesn't see this like I do. She says she's practical. I think she wants to believe. The first night he saw this woman, after Molly and I had just moved in, we were desperate. Mol walked the property looking for footprints with a flashlight. She said maybe we could draw a picture of her from his description. I called Watertables from the dark of the kitchen. I told them their mental patients were crossing the field and terrorizing my father. They said no way.

I decided he would sleep upstairs; Dad climbs stairs just fine. I said if he slept upstairs he couldn't claim this woman came to his window. Mol wouldn't budge. What if he should slip? What if he fell? Jim, she told me, your grandfather went and now your father is going. Deal with it.

I sip my coffee. It tastes salty. The well water always tastes salty during a dry spell. The announcer is running off lists of numbers, soy and pork bellies, steer futures. The prices seem low, though I am unsure. It's my job to know the cost of things. I remember back when I lived here as a boy, what Dad got a bushel then, which makes the numbers seem high. "He's just scared," I say. "That's all. He thinks we might put him in there."

She looks at me. "I talked to Litner," she says.

"No doctors, Mol. I'm serious." My father needs me, and that's okay. But I didn't come here for him. I came here for us. Mol says we have time, but we don't. We don't have any time for this.

Dad's up the landing with his head in the door. He's slumped in overalls and wearing the cap I gave him: Farmers Do It In The Dirt. "Paper's here," he says.

"Look like rain?" I ask. He looks at me like I'm foolish to have to ask someone else.

"Eggs?" Molly asks.

"Eggs are for birds," he says and walks out into the yard to read. Every morning she says eggs and he says birds. They have this together, her and him, these little jokes.

It's quiet after he's gone, just the radio. Out the window, I see him sit on a bucket under the tree. Near him, the rose leaves are coming in red, and past those are summer beans running downhill to the shade trees of No Show Creek. The beans look waxy. "Look," I say. "When I was a kid, there was only one rule: Don't go near the Watertables. Dale and I could jump off the barn, run the reaper, shoot the Damascus, anything. But stay clear of Watertables. He's always been afraid of it. Always."

"I'm just saying someone for him to talk to. It's not getting any better. What if it gets worse? What if you don't figure this out?"

"No doctors, Mol. He's never going in there. He's going to get old and read his paper and tell his stories and then he's going to die. Grandpa Jim dropped dead picking apples from that tree." I point out the window, but she won't look, especially with Dad sitting there. I don't want to argue. The coffee is getting cold. I drink my salty coffee and watch through the window the wind clipping his hair, his cuffs. It tries to take the paper from his hands. "Grandpa Jim started going when we were young. He told stories that didn't make sense. He always gave Dale bad advice and showed me how to do things wrong. But Dad helped us understand, made it okay, made us see it was just part of the deal."

"But that's not what you're doing, Jim," she says earnestly, softly. "You were yelling at him last night."

It's quiet again. Paul Harvey comes on the radio to tell us exactly how the world works. Mole-A-Way can rid our garden of pesky rodents through the use of undetectable sound waves, he tells us. Our turnips will be protected by modern technology. It worked for a woman in Lincoln he says. I trust Paul Harvey and I really want to believe he's right about a simple box saving my garden, about mysterious waves fixing my problems.

We both jump as Dad knocks on the window. It scares Molly for a second, him looking in like that, waving the newspaper.

I unlatch and open the window. "Je-sus," he says, handing me the article. "He paid his friend to cut his foot off to fool the insurance. Anybody ever try that on you?"

I look at the article. "No, Dad. I sell crop insurance. Remember?"

"Go ahead. Read it," he says returning to his bucket. "They ought to take those crazy birds out in the middle of nowhere and push 'em off a hill."

Molly laughs. She leans forward and whispers with her diluted Boston accent, "Where do you suppose he thinks the middle of nowhere is?" I miss her laugh. She has an honest laugh and it fades too soon.

I have been preaching pestilence for a full year and now it's all coming true. I've been talking men into banking on doom while I bet against it. But honestly I don't know the first thing about the weather. So I'm reading the almanac when Gene Allen comes into my office. He's wearing a short-sleeved, collared shirt with jeans and dirty penny loafers and seeing him in July means he's on his last leg.

The meteorologists in Omaha tell me forecasting's an art, at best. But my father could smell a cloud a week in coming. He'd step out into the blue sky, open white shirt and black boots laced with leather tails, jeans half buttoned, a bachelor eating a drumstick and squinting in the line-to-line arcing blue. He'd toss that bone and stand licking his fingers before buttoning his pants, squinting in the morning sun, a man about measuring. Then he'd tarp the hay. He'd shed the tractor and put up Grandpa's old mules, Miggs and Jenny. And Dale and I would leave our bicycles in the dirt approach, wheels spinning, to enter the fields and wait under a blue sun for a rain that must be coming.

That's how I remember him now as Gene takes a seat, my father seen from the broad-leafed beans below, a man on his property deciding, while I waited in the rows next to my brother for the first big drops to come out of nowhere to bend the dusty plants. Dad would say it was coming; Grandpa Jim could still tell you how much. Grandpa Jim got to where he couldn't figure out his shoes, but he'd clod onto the porch and say seven-tenths. Me, I'm betting. I lick my fingers and stare at the sky and see nothing. I see a crop-beating sun and dust. I hurry the book into a drawer; it's not something for me to be seen reading, not what I should be subscribing to.

Farmers today are like Gene, like me, guessing. Gene knows I'm from the big city. He thinks I have technology at my beck and call. Farmers want to know what satellites see and computers tell, but they're leery, too. They want me to be someone like them, someone they can trust. And, at the same time, they want me to be a distant expert with a clipboard and a phone link to Skylab. So I wear blue jeans and a cheap tie across a crisp white shirt. I drive a brand-new Chevy, but always with a bale or a barrel in back, sometimes planking. I sit in a rolled leather chair and watch Gene track dirt onto my carpet and I decide I'll leave that dirt there for a week, or longer, as a sign of that certain mix of hard work and prosperity that people want to believe in. We shake hands. He sets a bag of dirt on my desk. I test their soil in Dad's basement for free. I read a library book on how to do it, but my answer is always the same: fertilize, nitrates nitrates nitrates. Anything to ensure a yield.

"I got browntops all across and I can't keep the dirt on the ground for all this wind," he says and points toward my wall, toward the wind we both know is out there. "They say we're going to come up low on water this season, Jim. They say the rains aren't coming."

"A well's always the best bet," I say and I start my monologue: the cost of drilling and irrigation, numbers and statistics, fast mathematics and calculations, and I'm losing him, dazzling him into a slight stupor, which I want. I turn the computer screen to him and start running charts and graphs in the iridescent green. He holds his chair arms and watches my hands move. His father's land is his now. His father, who never once sought help and never took it, who Gene probably never once saw fearful of the future, of something that couldn't be helped, and now Gene's in my office pricing an easy way out, pricing safety. I add wind and hail and flood and tornadoes, my hands swirling above the desk. I talk of Chinese Moths and Cotton Weevils. There's blight and black root and hydrosemitis and I'm talking as if there are too many dangers to list when Molly calls. She tries to sound sincere as she asks me if fifth graders would know what magma was.

"Molly, I'm working on a policy here. I don't have time."

"I talked with Litner," she says. "Go see him today, he wants to speak with you about your father."

I don't say anything. I watch Gene read an article I cut out of the paper and taped to the wall. It's about the plains drought; the headline reads, "Farmers Lose Everything."

"I made an appointment for you."

I still don't say anything.

"Jim?" she says. Then she gets this talking-to-herself tone. "I'm trying to be understanding here. I'm trying to be wife-like about this."

"No way, Mol. You know how I feel. We talked about it. We're not seeing him. Dad's going to live with us and then he's going to teach his future grandkids how to whittle wrong and they're going to cut their fingers off, okay. One big happy thumbless family. No doctors."

Now she's quiet. Gene has turned from the article and is looking at me. In his pale eyes he seems lost and confused, like me. He doesn't want insurance but he's reached a point where he's prepared to pay. He eyes the headline again and I understand him for a moment, someone gotten to a place he doesn't know. I don't want to sell him a policy. I want to talk him out of it, to tell him to go home, to quit praying for rain. Quit praying, I think.

"Look," I say to her. "I can't see anyone today. After lunch I have to drive to Omaha to pick up the new trends. I have to have this month's rates out Monday."

"Come home for lunch."

I'm quiet. I tap my pencil on the desk so she can hear. Gene wants to leave so I mouth at him to sit.

"I'm working too. Just come home and we'll talk."

"Okay," I say, quieter. "You're right."

I can hear them talking on the other end. "Your father wants you to get him a beer on the way home. Any kind," she says. "No, it's a Coors now."

Gene, I realize, has my father's difficult eyes. They are grey and set in with lowering lids, searching eyes that roam the room for guidance. Troubled eyes lighten with age. Dad's are almost white. Gene shifts some and then stands, looking at his bag of dry dirt on my desk, looking for a sign telling him whether he should take his dust with him or not and I can only think that some day soon I will have those eyes.

"Did you look for the bag?"

"Yeah," she says. "I looked."

"Look again, okay?"

"It's not the bag," she says, and I tell her eleven and hang up.

Inside the No Show Tavern, I order three tenderloins, slaw, a six of Coors and a draft. Willert's youngest, Winston, sets the beer before me and I suck the cool foam.

I rent Dad's land to Willert for a third of the futures and Winston rolls up once in a while in a million-dollar Steiger to watch game shows in a climate-controlled cab as he cultivates the rows. He has walked into the cooler and I can see him looking out into the bar through frosted glass. I put a handful of plastic forks in my shirt pocket and I can see him stare at me through rows of brown bottles. He wipes the white from the glass with his hand, to see what else I may take. Sweat drips from my nose onto the bar. Even the beer tastes salty in this heat.

I set to thinking in the hot room. The windows are painted black. Fans turn fast and out of balance. On the wall is a picture of a penguin pointing to blue icicles dangling from the words Air Conditioning. I don't think about all the policies I'll have to pay, or the underwriter or Gene, a customer I was probably lucky to lose. I think about Molly, the way she's trying to humor Dad, like he was one of those kids in her textbooks. There's no humor in this. I know my Dad. He's just got to be shown there's nothing to fear. He sees that and this whole thing stops. I show him and it's over.

I call for another draft and Winston comes out of the cooler. His hair is frosted and his lips are pale, but he's still sweating. The tavern doors open as two, three, five men enter, a full crew dressed in brown with tan nametags, all with large key rings hooked in cracked belts. I look at my watch. Ten thirty. It's the third shift getting off from Watertables.

The end one has to take the stool next to me, which he doesn't seem to like, and he bumps me as he hunkers down. With his round face and his buzzed hair under a brown baseball cap, he's a guy I might have gone to school with. But then I see his boots; they're steel toed with the leather roughed at the tips, the metal showing. Winston starts pouring beers, lots of them, as they pass the dice cup in turn, shaking and spilling them onto the bar to see who'll pay. The end one begins clanking his steel toe against the brass rail like he's comforted by the sound. He turns to look at me. His nametag reads Shick, and Shick takes his time looking at my tie, the folders of papers on the bar, the bundle of plastic forks in my pocket. He catches me looking at those steel toes, clanking away at the rail. He scratches the scruff on his neck until he's taken things in and turns to talk Dakotadome football with the guy next to him. "...but the main problem with astro—"

"You work out there?"

Shick slowly rolls his head to me, mouth open. "Yeah," he says and swings back to the other guy, "—turf is that there's too much traction."

"You guys guards?"

Shick stops again. The guy on the other side of him shakes the dice cup and watches in the dark heat of the bar. His nametag says Lem, and he has a deep grooved face, like a poorly ironed shirt, which seems to crease and uncrease as he considers my question. His boots are similar except they're pointed.

"We're monitors," Shick says in the direction of Lem.

"Monitors?"

"Monitors make sure things go smooth."

I want to let all of this go, but I can't. "Then why the boots? They look all—"

"Oh that," he says and smiles. "That comes from kicking old people in the head." Then there's a quiet as he shakes the captain's cup and spills dice on the bar.

Lem laughs. The grooves loose then bind. "Tell him to piss off," he says to me. "Shick's just being an asshole. We use our boots to slow the tires on the wheelchairs. Like brakes. You know, it rubs the leather."

I smile a little easier now, relax some. I sip my beer and feel the joke, the way you want to trust a man who can put you off. I drink deeper than I normally would, a true gulp. "You got a woman in there named Margaret?" I ask Lem.

Shick has rolled triple twos. His big face studies the dice on the bar. Lem has to pay he decides and Shick calls out for another round.

"I don't know names," Lem says in a voice that you wouldn't know from his face. "Go to Divisions desk. There's a form you fill out."

"She's probably older, with longer hair maybe."

Suddenly Shick turns to me, as if he's noticed me for the first time. He eyes the forks in my pocket. "Look, you got someone in there or not?"

I pause. I can feel the fans whirring overhead. I open my mouth but everything I can think to say feels unfamiliar. My eye catches Winston in the cooler again, looking scared and angry through yellow glass the way my father did last night. "No. No I guess I don't."

"Then what the hell do you care?"

The bar is quiet and I want my food, I want to leave now. Three empty beer glasses sit on the bar before us. The dice are still. Then Shick shakes his head and starts to laugh, at first a low snorting sound through his nose. Lem smiles too and soon they're both laughing. Shick turns and laughs right at me, but it's as if he's saying none of this counts, and I start to smile. "I can't take it," he says. "That's a good one. Slows the wheelchairs. You kill me with that, Lem." I laugh with them for a moment until different punch lines begin to surface.

"Kick 'em in the head," Lem says and soon they are laughing so hard they forget where they are, babies, just the two of them, laughing and laughing.

I'm tired on the way home. Driving past the Watertables I feel the cool mist through the windows of their sprinklers running that long green lawn, bright water running in the middle of the day. I don't care about Omaha or the trends or my rates. Every policy I sell now is doom, and I know it. I just want to lie down and turn on the air conditioner. Up the approach my fenders rumble. One of the empty barrels bounces out, but I drive on, faster. Coming up the way, I see that the windows are open, the curtains blowing in from the screens. A big white house in a hot wind against a green field and blue sky. I don't want to fight.

When I park, I see Molly doing something I've never seen before. I grab the food from the seat and walk over. She is picking apples from Grandpa Jim's tree. She's set up a sort of picnic, a card table and chairs and iced tea in the shade of the tree. Mol has on sandals and a white cotton dress. She is using the front of her skirt to catch the fruit, and I sit and watch as she shows me the backs of her legs when she reaches. I pour a glass of iced tea and enjoy looking at her. I haven't looked at her this way in a while.

"The picnic looks nice," I say. "It was a nice idea."

She turns and says thanks and continues picking. "I think I'll make a pie. I've never made an apple pie before."

She comes over and lets the apples roll from her skirt onto the table. They make a pleasant sound, like bare feet on old floors. I lean back in the chair and decide I won't tell her they're crabapples. I decide right now I'll eat that pie. I pour her some tea. "Look, Molly. I know I've been a pain lately. I haven't been myself. The insurance, this thing with Dad. Maybe it's the weather. You know me. I get an idea in my head and it builds and builds. I just want to say this is a nice thing you did for us. I want to..." I stop and count. "Who's the fourth chair for?"

Molly's quiet. She pulls her hair back, exhales and shakes her head. "It's just a social call, Jim."

"Who's the chair for?" I'm standing now.

"He's doing us a favor. He's just coming by to...."

"Jesus Christ, Molly."

"There'll be no office or bill. He just wants to come by and see you two."

"Jesus." I shake my head. "I can't believe this."

"You're down there every other night, yelling. It's driving me crazy."

"It's driving you crazy?" I say, trying to lower my voice.

"Why not let him hear? You think he likes being yelled at less than whispered about?"

"He doesn't even know what's going on."

She turns her head and looks at something far off. "You really believe that?"

"No doctors, Molly. That's final." I point across the field. "It's just that place."

"No it's not, Jim," she says, slowly, looking at me. "It's you. He's fine with me all day. Something is happening with you two."

"There she is!" I hear him yell and I spin toward the house looking for my father. "I got her!" he says and suddenly I see his boots dangling off the roof. I see his hand lifted toward the Watertables.

I open the attic window and find him in the sun that is reflecting off the shakes. He is sitting on the edge of the roof, looking at Watertables with his long field glasses. A light film of dust has settled over him. I step out into the light. The shingles are shrinking, drying up, becoming loose. They shift and crack under me. A cornice of dust runs over the gable and turns at my feet.

"Dad," I say, trying to speak calmly, trying not to frighten him. "You need to come off the roof."

He turns, his white hair flips in the wind. "Call your old dad a liar will you? You'll see."

I step toward him. The silt is slick on the roof and I leave long footprints. His skin is pink. He has stopped sweating. "How long have you been up here?"

"As long as it takes." He lifts the binoculars again. I can see that he's got them all out of focus. "You bring the beer?"

"Yeah. It's downstairs. Let's go have a beer, okay?" I sit on the eaves next to him. "Come down with me."

"She's coming. You'll see."

"Dad, you can't do this to me." My eyes are hot and I rub them until they throb. My collar pops up. "Not in the daytime. You can't do this to me during the day."

"Do what?"

"This." I put my hands out. "This."

He shrugs. "My roof."

No matter what, I decide, I'm not going to get mad. No matter what.

"I think they're dancing," he says and passes the glasses to me. He puts them in my hands and explains, pointing, "See how they got them gardens set? Don't have that damn hedge in the way. That's where they've got 'em. In circles, dancing around. It's crazy, isn't it? You wouldn't catch me dancing with those birds. Go on, look."

I don't even want to touch the glasses. I force them back into his determined fingers.

"Are they dancing?" he says, looking at the binoculars. "Tell me if they're dancing."

"No. We're going to get off the roof. It's not safe up here."

"Oh no. No way." He loops the binocular strap around my neck and they fall against my stomach.

I kick at the edge of the roof and a shingle falls and turns in the wind to snap on the rider mower. "See Dad, they're so dry they're falling out. There isn't any rain."

"Gonna rain tomorrow."

I wave my hand at the sky above us. I'm so frustrated I can't even seem to shake words out.

"I know," he says.

"No you don't know, Dad!" I yell. "You don't know."

"You read the barometer? Mostly I use that," he says and I

want to just pick him up and carry him in. The barometer hasn't changed in weeks. "See them heifers over at the fence, eyeing that alfalfa?" he says pointing. "Those are Willert's cows. Ain't seen them in a couple of weeks have you? They're four miles from the tank. It's a good sign. You check your gauge. It'll change."

"That's it, that's your answer? You watch the cows?"

"Your Grandpa Jim did. Like I said, I prefer the barometer."

"This isn't cows, Dad. This is serious. I mean this is really serious." I look up at the sky, the encompassing blue. Not a cloud. Below I see Molly gazing up with me, her hand shading her eyes.

"Boy she's hot," he says and for a minute I think he means Molly, who I'm thinking of. Molly, who I'm watching back slowly into the beanfield to get a better view of us, and I think god if he sees her out there it's over.

Dad wipes the dirt from his forehead and I motion with my hand to flag her out of the field. She waves back, a small movement at her waist, as if she were afraid of being seen as encouraging, and suddenly I am afraid of her. But he won't let up. "You look in those glasses and tell me what you see. You look and we'll go."

I lift the rims to my brow but I can't look.

"Are they dancing?"

"Yeah," I tell him, my eyes closed. "It looks like they're dancing."

Dad squints at me in disbelief. "You're lying, aren't you?"

"No."

He opens his mouth. "You, you did it again, didn't you?"

This is funny to him. He gets the craziest look on his face. His pale eyes widen with surprise. No, I say but he's laughing now, I mean, he's really funny. I start to smile. I almost can't help it because I haven't seen him smile in so long, but I look into his failing eyes and it is not funny.

"You did. You lied," he says, shaking his head, shifting his hip to stand. "Three times." And before I know it, he's walking toward the window with his head listing, laughing softly in the wind and I feel, as I look from my father to my wife in the rustling green, that some unseen force holds me just beyond them.

I help him across the pitch and guide his unsteady foot over the sill. I stop at the window, though. There is a glimmer in the beans which catches my eye, a quick flash, and I start to lift the glasses. I don't know anymore. The scary thing is I truly don't know what I'll see. It could be my forks in a beanrow or Litner dusting up my drive. It could be rainclouds on the horizon. I stand on the roof gripping those black frames and I honestly can't tell you if I'm searching for a woman in blue paper dancing with my gym bag or for a boy crouched in the beans, a boy who's been told the future and still believes.

This is **Adam Marshall Johnson**'s first publication.

"Dad, the World Wide Web is definitely not a sequel to Charlotte's Web."

STA. LUCIA / *Jennifer Gage*

The diffuse climate of afterlife opens *God*
is light and closes *in him*
is no darkness the hinge
of Lucia's belief an aberrant

photosensitivity she still finds
troublesome this morning for instance
hay bales were steady vortexes
of brightness yellow in the field as

competing suns the air about them
already shot through with winter in
precarious suspension she watched
three vultures light as birds

are said to do unsettling on them with
strange gravity the day the moment
they went down revealing
a dark tear bird shaped where

God had perched Lucia thought
this another cheap trick
of light a sign perhaps
but nothing to put weight on no

shoulder or thinking of her
lover his name his face long
gone no hand to place a ring
on like the one hollow in

candlelight he held out and mistaking it
for a moth beating with stunned wings
an orbit of desire *no* out of mercy
for the dying thing she told him *no*.

STA. LUCIA CRITIQUES HER
CHILDHOOD / *Jennifer Gage*

In the orchard, as you might imagine, the light was cadenced. Insatiable. Even so, I had my questions. I questioned the leaves for falling. The apples fell too but no one, I noticed, said *in a perfect collision no energy would be lost.* Did you know that each item of belief alters the mind's topography, that is, refolds each convolution? To me, next to this, the bruises were only secondary concerns. A difference slight but palpable. I think that this is what is meant by *habit of mind,* as in *we could always save these for applesauce.* I like to think that these thoughts expand me, or my mother, at least, who taught me. To illustrate: one day my brother caught his gym bag in the spokes of his bike and lay not unconscious, exactly, but quietly bleeding until a policeman brought him home. I believe I was downstairs when she called me into the kitchen, which was cluttered with her sobs and his and mine when she said *Look. I want you to look at this.* The point is there was no point to this. To anyone else the impact alone would have been enough, but she called me in, as a witness to what was lost. And as you might imagine, this caused me some trouble later. A friend once asked, *When you fly, don't you want to jump right out onto the clouds?* I believe he began hating me then, that day when I told him how really I worried the planes might tear or stretch them beyond all recognition. He said, he practically screamed at me, *Don't you have any imagination at all? Can't you ever think of anything different?* But the truth was, I couldn't. The truth was, there really weren't any bikes back then, or planes either, and I sat in our orchard all the fall days long, anxiously scanning a clear blue sky.

STA. LUCIA SHEDS LIGHT ON THE ART OF
BUON FRESCO / *Jennifer Gage*

"Love is not consolation, it is light." Simone Weil

1.

With the Lord a day
is like a thousand years, and a thousand years
are like a day.

2.

The boy was ten or twelve.
His mother popped in to buy milk or bread, he
    wasn't sure.
They were waiting for her.
I want to see one of you ride that horse said father
    from the front seat, nodding to
    a coin-operated pony ride by the entrance. He
    was funny like that.
In the long pause mother wasn't there. His
    brother small beside him.
There was a nickel in his hand.
There was a nickel in his hand, waving.
Mother's eyes. *What's going on?* Staring, her eyes,
    milk in her hands.
No one's going anywhere until I see— The boy was ten or
    twelve. The door was
    open and he was running, nickel in his hand. From
    the car his brother stared and his father stared and
    his mother and the pony wide-eyed and it began to
    bounce up and down and he was staring too but he
    did not get on.
They drove home.

3.

Each a brushstroke silting in his wrists,

4.

a certain mineral ache: antimony
yellow, raw sienna, lapis lazuli,
white lime; cantina walls the color of
pink bismuth, a stalled bus; green
issue of its driver, cursing, cursing,

5.

until each gesture fused to its ground like skin, subject
to its disasters, crumbling,
dampness, and

6.

its paradoxical necessity. In memory's
humid grasp, calla lilies
scroll around each sun-
stained sex, each white hand cupping
a fevered eye,

7.

stalks erect, the rows regular as corn, and as familiar:

8.

echoing the tiller's design: *In the beginning
was the Word and the Word was*

9.

an act of speech in time, coded according to a prede-
termined system as a series of marks on paper. After
pricking the outline and laying it to the wall, he subjects
it to a process known as *pouncing*, repeatedly passing
a cloth sack filled with charcoal powder over the tiny
punctures until enough dust seeps through to transfer
the image

10.

the endless postures of sacrifice which entreat him:
   One look
at his face as he walks past, for instance, and a woman
calls out after him *I could find you, oh!*

11.

(she *calls out*, her sincerity an accent in itself)

12.

a very nice t-shirt for you! Or an Indian,
too young for love but old enough to know that need
repeats itself, settling each morning's weight on her
shoulders, a wool wrap, croons insistently *comprarlo*, her
words spinning sky-blue thread, *comprarlo*, spinning, *buy it*,

13.

buy it, though he cannot quite, this woman, this
figment of the imagination probably, a real
work of art: sifting his life for semi-
precious stones, grinding them to a powder: her eye
for color, their proportions: each time a perfect
match: the exquisite concealment

14.

of joints. "Ultimately, deconstruction
would have you put everything in
scare quotes." He paints, certain
someone said this once, her emerging
torso a sort of complicity, "a shattered bit

15.

of rib" brush tonguing
shadows, "a bell jar"
spelling the cleft between her
breasts, "a hoop skirt" dimple of
clavicle, yes, rendering all "a free
agent" her secret names

16.

as pendulum arcs, crow's feet, blue symmetry
of hips beneath a Tzotzil's shawl, each eye
in her outstretched palm glittering,
a coin, torn out,
torn out

17.

as she will not be, yesterday's *intonaco* already un-
yielding as bone, a relic,

18.

or a contest of wills. Often he'll find her, unbidden,
     translated
across time zones to his kitchen, where she stands
     eyeing him
silently, toasting a bagel, red tile solid beneath her feet.

STA. LUCIA ENCOUNTERS MECHANICAL DIFFICULTIES / *Jennifer Gage*

In Chomula, state of Chiapas, all the saints
hold mirrors. Each prayer directed at their silver
backs bounces back, the possibility of justice
they offer remaining all it ever was, reflexive,
an activity of the eyes. They talked to God once
then died. Lucia wanted more. Far away, caught
in mortal traffic, she eases her truck into
third behind four Model T's, Upper Ohio
Valley Auto Club signs stuck in their high
back windows. Second. The hill gives way
to their tires, but slowly. They are driven
by men, Lucia sees, pleased as they are with
this made-to-order day and how it unrolls
through their windscreens, sepia tinted, a set
for movies fraught with mine collapse and family
illness, but ultimately happy. Time passes.
No one is late for anything. She wants to shake
their hands, though their habit is no doubt flawless
execution, a well-oiled machine. The road grows
a shoulder and ahead is the rest of their party,
parked, Lucia imagines, so the ladies can buy
potted herbs from a curbside nursery. She drives
past, counting. Twelve jewel-toned relics. Lucia
is beyond them before the image of the first
car reaches her brain, steam roiling from its
open hood, an icon of perfect failure. She
thinks she should do something. In the rearview
her eyes hang and the driver stands loosely
watching, knees bent, engine cooling in the clear sky.

13 DECEMBER / *Jennifer Gage*

Begin with the commonplace. Walk in to the thin
light of afternoon, which will lead you to your love

of absolutes, the coldest night, the blackest night,
for instance, or the night long coming. There are trolls

underfoot. There is a doe you keep flinging up
against barbed wire with the shock of your eyes

alone. Can you believe in anything so purely
pagan? Have you room in your bag for an apple?

The things you feed will not leave you, not the horses
rushing to the farthest reach of the top pasture,

not the red-tailed hawk, its cry a descent
you've imagined endlessly into the draining sky.

Look, these are the same old dogs emerging from the
same old woods, and the sun's dark habit is nothing

personal. Familiar words are collecting beneath
each tongue. Unrest, I insist, is a loose translation.

PILGRIMAGE, LOUISIANA / *Jennifer Gage*

My Father described these lean figures, the shape I'm in,
bodies hard-muscled and unswerving as girls. In spring
earliest leaves obscure the first blurs of breast, they rise
from the river that carried them, a steady green line;
black willows along Interstate 10, tipping like nuns.

Still, who could expect what they've led to, young boys
under slack June heat, dancing before an open box,
their taps pinging in the sun. Somewhere there is a shrine
I could pin body parts to, elbows and necks and
this leg hung over Bourbon Street, just kicking around.

MILAGROS / *Jennifer Gage*

One day, Lucia and I went searching for milagros,
                                        sweet
annunciations of tin, feet-shaped or else hearts or arms.
Any thin human form like the ones
                              the faithful have left here
on your lush velvet backdrop would do. A child with boots
puddled in the afternoon
                        rain was cupping a dying
language in her upturned palms, the lot behind her family's
    shack
heaped with empty Coke bottles. A clue. For this I paid
                                        a peso, certain
she'd met the smiling brown-faced man pictured with his
    pegboard
of charms. He could be close
                              at hand, selling the dangling pleas
of chronic bleeders, the halt and purblind on the next street
or the next. I decided to send this image
                              to friends with the usual
pleasantries on the back, *having a great time, will write more*
soon, love, wondering if he stamped or molded these prayers,
and who would appreciate them most.
                              All day I sought
. miracles, craving their smooth, barely perceptible weight.
                                                    Eyes
in your hands, you know this lust, the gravity that pins
a body down, the blended cries of gratitude and
                              anguish, its mate.

Jennifer Gage, our Tom McAfee Discovery Feature poet, received her MA in English from Ohio University. She taught English for two years in a public high school in Baton Rouge and currently works at the American School of the Hague in the Netherlands. These are her first published poems. Another poem from this sequence will appear in Antioch Review.
The Tom McAfee Discovery Feature is a continuing series to showcase the work of an outstanding new poet who has not yet published a book. The prize is funded by the family and friends of Tom McAfee.

Larry Brown

© Bruce Newman

Larry Brown lives in Oxford, Mississippi, where he was born and raised. He joined the Marine Corps during the Vietnam War and, after returning home, worked for the Oxford Fire Department for seventeen years. He resigned in 1990 to write full time. Brown is the author of four books of fiction, *Facing the Music, Dirty Work, Big Bad Love* and *Joe*, which won the 1992 Southern Book Critic's Circle Award for Fiction. He is also the author of a memoir, *On Fire*.

This interview was conducted by Kay Bonetti for the American Audio Prose Library in June of 1995 at the Center for the Study of Southern Culture in Oxford, Mississippi. AAPL has produced recordings of readings by and interviews with 130 distinguished authors. For information call 1-800-447-2275 or write AAPL at PO Box 842, Columbia, MO 65205.

An Interview with
Larry Brown / *Kay Bonetti*

Interviewer: You list your hometown as Oxford, Mississippi, where you're still living and worked as a firefighter for sixteen years. Did you actually grow up in the city or out in the country?

Brown: I was born in Oxford at the old hospital up the street from the courthouse, but we lived about twelve miles out in the country. We moved to Memphis when I was about three years old. I lived there ten years and went to school in Memphis until the eighth grade, which was in '64, and then we moved back to Mississippi, and I've been out around here all the time since then, for the last thirty-one years.

Interviewer: What took your family up to Memphis?

Brown: My father came out of World War II in '45, and he farmed for a good long while, but he was having all of us, and just really couldn't make a go of it farming. He had a good job waiting for him at Fruehauf Trailer Company in Memphis so we moved up there. By that point there were six of us altogether, my mother and my daddy and my two brothers and my sister. We had a growing family in a short length of time. I was born in '51. My father came out of the war in '45, and my sister and one of my brothers are older than me.

Interviewer: I understand your mother was a postmistress?

Brown: She did that part-time until she retired. We had a little store out at Tula that Mary Annie and I ran for a couple of years. Mother would come in and take care of the mail every day. The Postal Service was threatening to close the Post Office unless we could move it into a building that stayed open all day long, so I went over and took all the stuff and moved it into my store, and nailed it all back together, and we opened the Post Office in the store. We've still got it out there, too.

Interviewer: Is that the store you've modeled John Coleman's store in *Joe* and the store in the story "Old Soldiers" with Mr. Aaron on?

Brown: Actually, ours was a relatively new building. The store that's in my books was torn down some time around 1966 or '67, and had been there for a long time. It had the pot-bellied stove and the patches of tin on the floor, and all the bottlecaps just ground into the sand, hundreds and hundreds and hundreds of them, and the old slick benches out front that had been whittled and had people's initials in them because they'd been used for years.

Interviewer: Where did the love of books and reading come from?

Brown: Mainly from my mother. One of my earliest memories is of seeing her reading. There were always books in our house. I just grew to love it real early, I guess—escaping into stories and discovering other worlds. When I was a child I was a big reader of Greek mythology. I actually read a lot of literature without knowing what I was doing, because Mother bought a set of encyclopedias, and there was a set of ten classics that came with it. There was Edgar Allan Poe, and Mark Twain, and Zane Grey, and Herman Melville, and Grimms' Fairy Tales, and Greek mythology, the Iliad and the Odyssey, and Jack London. That's eventually what brought me to writing—loving to read.

Interviewer: Was there a point when you started separating things out and making distinctions of taste?

"I make up all my characters out of little bits and pieces of real life."

Brown: I don't think I did until around 1982. I had been writing for about two years, pretty much on my own. I had published one short story in *Easy Riders' Motorcycle Magazine*. That was my first publication. I was really desperate for some help. So I came out here and went to a writing class that Ellen Douglas taught at the University. She pointed me toward a lot of things that I hadn't seen before, like the work of Joseph Conrad and Dostoevski and Flannery O'Connor. It was around that time that I began to discover what kind of writer I wanted to be. I had read Faulkner when I was sixteen years old. I really didn't think too much about it, except that "The Bear" was a great hunting story. It was only when I got older that I could appreciate all the other things that story was about, like the encroaching of industry upon the forest, and the way things were changing and all this happening as this young boy comes of age. The gradual reduction of the wilderness, just by the railroad coming through, and people beginning to log the timber off. All that was real saddening once I grasped it later on, but it was only after I started writing that I was fully able to appreciate the value of that story.

Interviewer: You must have recognized it because of the landscape.

Brown: Very much so. It was all very familiar to me. It was right up my alley. When I was sixteen that's what I wanted to do—stay in the woods with my gun and hunt every day and half the night sometimes, too.

Interviewer: I gather that you didn't much like school.

Brown: No, I didn't. I was such a poor student that I failed English my senior year and had to go to summer school to get

> *"It's fascinating to know that people were down here in Mississippi building homes and raising families back when the Constitution was being written."*

---

my diploma. I didn't graduate with the rest of my class. It was very disappointing to my mother.

Interviewer: Why was that? Was it just attitude?

Brown: It was probably a combination of losing my father when I was sixteen and never having any interest in school to begin with. The only interest I had was in getting out of school, getting a job and buying a car, because I didn't have any way to go anywhere. I always had to catch rides with somebody else. I was just itching to get out on my own and start making a living. I didn't think that the future looked very bright at that point anyway because the war was going on. All the boys I grew up with were worrying about it. We'd already had some friends who'd gone over and been killed. I pretty much knew that I was going to have to go into the service at the height of the Vietnam War. I didn't have any long-range plans. I didn't see too much reason to worry a whole lot about what happened in school.

Interviewer: Is Walter James' story in *Dirty Work*, at least in terms of the going away, close to your story?

Brown: In some ways. Of course my father was already gone, then. But one thing that struck me, and why there are references to my father in there, was I saw what a tremendous sacrifice he had made, and that veterans of the Vietnam War made. War is an awful thing, and I didn't understand exactly what his life had been like until I heard him talk about all the hardships that he'd suffered, and how lucky he'd been to come out at the other end of it alive. The guys in *Dirty Work* are actually based on some disabled Marines that I met in the early '70s in Philadelphia where

---

I was stationed—guys who were in wheelchairs, who had lost their arms and legs and had made that great sacrifice, too.

Interviewer: You were in the Marines during the period of the Vietnam War. Why didn't you get sent overseas? Was it just the luck of the draw?

Brown: I just lucked out. Around the time that I went in, October of 1970, some of the troop withdrawals had already started. Now the Marines' policy—I didn't know this when I went in—is, they're the first in, they're the first out, too. A lot of the people who were getting pulled back were in the Marine Corps. The troop involvement was winding down. There were still a few people getting sent over, but from my platoon of thirty-eight men, probably only four or five had to go.

Interviewer: How did you spend your time in the Marines?

Brown: I went to the big base at Camp LeJeune, North Carolina first. Then I got orders to go to Marine Barracks, which is the oldest post in the Marine Corps. It was founded in 1776. It's what they call a Dress Blues station. They issue you a set of dress blues—you've seen these Marines with blue pants and tunics? What you do is a lot of official duty. There's a big naval shipyard there. You christen ships, you march in parades, you have to be on all this spit-and-polish detail—things like that.

Interviewer: But you met some disabled vets.

Brown: We had a NCO club behind our barracks. These guys would come over in their wheelchairs, and there was a set of steps there, four or five high. We'd just roll their wheelchairs up those steps and push them back there with us. There were two guys I was most impressed by. One of them didn't have any legs at all, but he had a pair of artificial legs, with pants on and tennis shoes on the bottom. He would come in on a pair of crutches, and you couldn't tell he didn't have any legs. He'd sit up on a bar stool and order a beer. The other guy had the kind of injury that Walter has. He had been shot all the way through the base of his skull. To look at him, he didn't have any kind of disfiguring wound. He was a nice-looking young man about twenty-one or twenty-two years old. But he had blackouts, seizures. They could control it somewhat with medicine, but not to the point where he could remain on active duty. So here was a nice, good-looking young guy walking around, twenty-two years old, on a hundred percent disability for medical problems. All that stuff is based on these real people.

Interviewer: How did you get to know them that well?

Brown: We were Marines, too. We were Marines and these guys were all Marine Corps veterans, and they were attached to the naval hospital there. I guess they got passes to leave their ward—the ones who were mobile. My friend with the artificial legs had his car fixed up with hand levers. He'd drive himself around, wherever he wanted to go. He had a girlfriend and lived a pretty normal life. That's where all that came from. All the stuff about the weapons and the war I either learned as part of my training, or from talking to veterans of the war. The whole Marine Corps was full of them. The sergeants and everybody were all veterans. Everybody you talked to—the officers—had already been over there and served and come back and been decorated. They were all full of stories. The Marine Corps is full of history. It has a really

"I'm interested in the way people get through their lives. I listen to people and wonder what they're about."

---

proud tradition, and they teach you about the great battles the Marines have fought in. They show you footage of the first day at Iwo Jima, when they shelled Mount Suribachi for two weeks, and then the first wave went out from those ships and there were three thousand U.S. Marines mowed down and killed the first day—in one day three thousand of them died. You see all that and you get indoctrinated into it. It just becomes a way of life.

Interviewer: You said "I put my father in *Dirty Work*" in that scene between Walter and his dad. To what extent is the portrait of the father in that novel a portrait of your own dad?

Brown: In little ways, here and there. My father never killed anybody and went to the penitentiary or anything. I make up all my characters out of little bits and pieces of real life. But I would like to think that if he and I had been allowed to have that conversation, if he had lived long enough to see me go in, the conversation would have been like that: he would have told me to be careful, and watch out, to try to come back home.

Interviewer: What about the man that runs that country store in Tula—the John Coleman and Mr. Aaron character in "Old Soldiers"? Is that a tribute to, or a portrait of, somebody you know?

Brown: Yes. His name was Norman Clark. He had the store there. He came out of the war just about the same time my father did and he never went anywhere after that. At one point he had a brand-new four-door 1962 Chevrolet Impala. That car sat right across the road and rotted into the ground. There was a period of twelve years when he never left Tula, and Tula's only a few

---

"This is my landscape and I love this place. I try to recreate it on the page."

---

hundred yards long. He stayed in that store every day for thirty-something years.

Interviewer: Did he have sixty-thousand dollars in a bank bag? That's what John Coleman says he has in his bank bag when he goes off in the truck—to Joe Ransom's surprise he agrees to go for a ride with him.

Brown: He had more than that! Somebody would bring a check in and say, "Can you cash this check for me, Norman?" He'd say, "Yes." They'd say, "Well, that's a pretty big check now. Sure you can cash it?" He'd say "Yeah." It didn't matter how big the check was, he could cash it. He had the money in there. And he had that pistol, too. Everybody knew it. He kept his Budweiser in the candy case, too. He didn't mind drinking it hot.

Interviewer: How often do you take people out of the community and out of your life, and transform them into your work?

Brown: In this particular case it was somebody I cared a whole lot about, because I can remember being a little bitty boy and going in his store. He would give me a little pack of candy corn and make some kind of joke about a rooster pecking, or something like that. But then I grew up and spent a lot of time with him. If you went in there by yourself and nobody else was there he would sit down and talk to you and tell you stories. He would tell these great war stories, just like my daddy. But if one other person was there he wouldn't do it. It had to be you and him. I stayed up at the store a lot. It was a little bitty place we lived in. There wasn't much to do sometimes, in the summer. Then I went into the service and came back out. I married and began to

---

raise a family, and he was *still* there in the store. He just died a few years back, from a war wound. He got blood poisoning from a piece of shrapnel that was in one of his leg bones that they never got out.

Interviewer: Is that a sensitive issue for you—using people in your fiction that are modeled on people out of your own life?

Brown: Not really. Even though characters may sometimes be based on real people, what happens is that the story around them will be different. The events will be different and they won't do the same things in my story that they did in real life. They might have a similar lifestyle, but I will invent the rest.

Interviewer: What about the family cemetery, the old house in *Joe*, where the Jones family is squatting. That's the Coleman Place. You figure that out as you're reading the book. Are that little springhouse and the well-tended gravesite there real?

Brown: They're all real but they're in different places. The log house was down on a place called Neal Hill many years ago when I used to hunt down there. It's since been bulldozed down. The grave was something that a friend and I found out in the middle of the woods one day deer hunting up in the National Forest. There was no structure anywhere around, just these weird little plants like a little protective garden, right in the middle of all these big trees. Just one grave. And the springhouse is something that I remembered from years and years ago. I had a friend, an older fellow I used to coon hunt with all the time. He had an old springhouse on his place. It was ice cold. You don't see those things anymore.

Interviewer: The interesting thing about the use of a detail like that in the novel *Joe* is the kind of atmosphere or reverberation that it helps to create in the character John Coleman. And by extension, in Joe as well. It makes the region and this community really sing.

Brown: It's a way to establish history and give some depth to the background of the people. There are old cemeteries scattered in the woods out where I live. Some of the stones go back to the 1700s. These communities died out for some mysterious reason a long time ago. But it's fascinating to me to know that this country was being settled back when the Constitution was being written—that there were people down here in Mississippi, living and building homes and raising families and pretty much exploring this whole country, which was a big wilderness back in those days.

Interviewer: You also move the story, explore character and, in the case of *Joe*, illuminate the landscape through the world of work. Larry Brown seems to be a person who is fascinated with the daily details of physical work.

Brown: I think it's a hard thing for a man to have to get up every morning and work hard doing some kind of physical labor, like swinging a hammer, all day long. I've had to do that so much myself to support my writing habit. Writing didn't bring in any money. I was doing it all the time, but I wasn't selling anything. I couldn't just come home from the Fire Department and sit down and write because I had three children to feed. So I'd have to do stuff like build houses and tote bricks, and haul hay, and deaden timber and sack groceries and all the other things that I did. I'm well versed in what hard work is. I really admire the people who

"I'm concerned with family connections. That's like a nest you go back home to every night."

---

do it. A lot of people turn their backs on it, and lay out or become bums or something.

Interviewer: It's interesting how you use it to illuminate character. You learn a lot about Joe Ransom's history from him banging out the fender on that old GMC truck. He says, "I used to be a body man." You wonder if it was in prison or not. The point is, that moves the relationship between him and Gary at that point in the story. It also shows keen observation of detail on your part.

Brown: I listen to people, and I look at their lives and wonder what they're about. Then I begin exploring. I put a character in a situation and I know that I have to have some kind of trouble going early on to involve me in the story, because I'm interested in the way people get through their lives. Joe has had all this stuff happen to him. He's lost his family, his son won't even speak to him, he's been in the penitentiary. He lives by himself. And he's got this work ethic too. He believes that a man ought to get up and go to work every morning.

Interviewer: And he makes a good living.

Brown: He's lucked out and got this job which pays very well, but he has to think about what he's doing, which is killing a living organism, a living forest. He's not happy with what he's doing, but it's a job. I guess he looks at it maybe, "If I don't do it, somebody else will. It's going to get done."

Interviewer: The narrator says, through his point of view, that he's thinking about what he's doing. What is it, in the larger sense of the word?

"Tragedy is inevitable in my stories because of the circumstances people live in."

Brown: The major thing, I think, is destroying the habitat for a whole bunch of wildlife. Hardwood forests support so many different forms of life: deer, turkey, squirrels, all the birds and insects and reptiles that live there. It's a renewable crop every year, this food that comes from oak trees and beech trees and all. The animals gather that up. Squirrels hide it. Predators find their prey there. Hawks and owls and all different forms of life are there. Man uses it to get food from, too. All that gets cut down, and you come back and plant a pine tree on it, and the only thing it bears is a pine cone, with a few little seeds in it. Once you lose that hardwood forest you've lost it forever, because they take so long to grow. You can have a pine plantation ready to harvest in about twenty years. You probably won't have even the first crop of acorns off of oaks until they're thirty years old. Once they're established, and they keep getting bigger and bigger, they provide a huge canopy from the sun. It's shady down there, right now, in the middle of the day, at three-thirty in the afternoon. Leaves fall year after year and choke out the small undergrowth. The big trees are left, and it's just like a floor. The beauty of a hardwood forest to me is unmatched. I think that's what Faulkner was talking about so long ago when he said that the land would accomplish its own revenge on the people. That's true. All that forest has largely disappeared, except for some privately held tracts of land in Lafayette County and what's available up on the National Forest. It's gotten to the point now where if you want to hunt you've got to either own some land or be in a hunting club. Things have really changed from what they were when I was eighteen years old and could hunt anywhere in this county I wanted to, and nobody would tell me there's a posted sign over there.

Interviewer: To what extent were you trying to call attention to issues like that in *Joe?*

Brown: I used to do that for a part-time living. I'm not proud of what I did. I did it simply for the money, to feed my family. I deadened timber in the springtime and the summer, and planted the pines in the winter. It's brutal work. A lot of people can't do it. They come out one day and quit at the end of that day. It's a tough thing to get out there at daylight when it's ten degrees, and work all day setting those pine trees. And it's tough to get out there at six in the summertime, in May, and go down through the woods and run into snakes and yellow jackets and spiderwebs. *Joe* gave me a great opportunity to show the landscape, and to set my characters against it. And to have this larger thing, even larger than the lives that are going on, which is the land. The ground is so ancient. It's the oldest thing we've got. I like to have people picture what it looks like—that distant watershed where all the lines of trees fade into this little blue line that's the end of the horizon. That's what I love. This is my country, and I love this place. I try to recreate it on the page.

Interviewer: In your book on firefighting, called *On Fire*, you imagined a scene, or you saw this family walking down the road. It became the Jones family walking down the road in the opening pages of *Joe*. Was that the germ of the novel?

Brown: Yes. I started writing it around 1984 or 1985, after I had already written five bad novels and thrown them all away. I burned one of them in the back yard. That was the first image that I had. The image of that family came before Joe came. Later on I invented my protagonist. But the opening shot that I wanted was that family walking down that hot blacktop road through a deserted landscape in the middle of the summer, with no place to go.

Interviewer: Where did Joe come in? How did he get in the mix?

Brown: He came as a way to try to save Gary from what his fate would have ordinarily been—probably something bad on down the road somewhere. The kid has never really been given a chance, and his father's not good. I wanted him to have a chance at a relationship with—not another father, but somebody who could take care of him for a little while. Joe was invented to do that. In the course of working on the story about him, I began to find out that his story was important, too. He had to have a background, a history, a future. This timber job was a logical thing for him to have. He'd lived a good bit of his life already. He'd already had other jobs. He'd had family. And now this is what he was left with. He was left with this job and a dog. That's really all that he has. Once in a while he has a woman, but he doesn't care too much about that. He cares about taking care of the future and trying to get through his life without going back to the penitentiary.

Interviewer: Which he probably fails at, ultimately.

Brown: Yes.

Interviewer: What fascinates me about the Jones family is that in spite of the horribleness of their background and their history, and all the things that have been going on throughout their life, they're a family. That's what pulls Gary back, tragically, into that milieu. The question of family and community is apparently very important to you. It's underneath everything you do, in your short stories and in the novels.

Brown: I'm concerned very much with family connections, relatives,

"Poverty causes terrible tragedies because poor people are the ones who live in firetraps."

and all that. That's like a nest you go back home to every night. You have these people around who are going to be with you all your life—the person you picked to marry, and your children. Your grandchildren are going to come from them, and you had the family that you came out of. And your mother had the family she came out of, and your father, on down the line. The Joneses are dysfunctional as a family, but still they're a unit. Fay takes it as long as she can, and then she goes. She's seen some of the others leave, too. Gary is young enough to remember Calvin. What happened to him and all. Putting all that in just illustrates how hopeless Gary's case is. I wanted him to have a chance. When you're writing something you never know how these things are going to turn out. When it came time to finish this novel, I wrote the ending of *Joe* about five different times.

Interviewer: You rewrote the ending five times? Different outcomes?

Brown: Different outcomes. One was a happily-ever-after where everything was hunky-dory. But the question that I ultimately had to ask myself was do the guilty always get punished in life, or do the innocent sometimes have to catch some stuff? And I said, in the real world they do, and if your fiction really imitates life, that's what you have to go with. I build my stories, and I try to be authentic in them. I sometimes get accused of being brutal and having a dark vision. That may be true. I don't know why my stuff is so dark. Except that I believe the whole process is just an attempt to pull the reader into the story, like I said a while ago. To make him forget that he's reading. Tragedy is inevitable in my stories, because of the circumstances people live in. I think my characters, most of them, know the difference between right and wrong. Certainly Wade knows the difference between right

"You start out writing and you don't know how bad you are."

and wrong. So does Joe. But doing those things—that's where you come to grips with your characters, how they react in certain situations.

Interviewer: Along with family, community is extremely important in your work. But the community is implied. It's interesting that you look at community from the points of view of those who are in fact, as you said in one of your short stories, living separate in the same house on badly eroded land, in a house of poor quality. I'm curious about that. Why do you choose to look at the issue of family and community from the broken side?

Brown: If Joe was a regular family guy he wouldn't have been involved in all this drinking and fighting and messing around with the police—all the things that he's done that have given him such a reputation and made every lawman around know him. He has a code of his own that he goes by. You have to respect him or fight him if you're going to tangle with him. I made his life the way it is to give the reader a sense early on of the brokenness of his life, and the amount of time he spends alone in that house listening to the tape player over and over again, watching junk on television that he doesn't even like, eating poorly, drinking way too much, smoking all these cigarettes, and all the carousing that he sometimes does. He has periods when he can do fine. He can go to work every day and go home and sleep every night. Then he has other times when he starts drinking and he gets in trouble. He starts running into people and making mistakes, and he has to start paying for all his mistakes again. Then he becomes partially involved with this kid, Gary. He becomes concerned about him and sees what the old man's doing to him, sees it the first day that he pays the kid off. He knows that the boy's old man, Wade, is going to take every penny the kid made that day. The way he looks at it is that there's no sense in paying him to work if Wade is going to take it anyway. "It's too painful to watch and I don't want to have to watch it because I know what's going to happen." But a little later he thinks, "If he won't bring his old man back, maybe he'll have a chance." Things get a little better and he says, "Maybe I can sell him my truck. He'll have a ride," and all this. Then he begins to find out more: how the kid can't read, doesn't know what a church is, how ignorant he is of the world around him, the things that other boys around him take for granted.

Interviewer: One reader has pointed out that another tragedy is that what Joe passes on in his initiation—such as it is—to Gary is the torch of some of his most destructive and worst habits, especially alcohol. I assume you would say, "That's the way it goes. That's the way things do tend to work themselves out." Nothing's wasted in this book, so you must have been keenly aware of the irony there.

Brown: Yes. Whatever kind of deal Gary is going to get out of Wade is going to be rotten. His father won't even defend him when some guy is beating him up. Even though he's in kind of rough hands, with Joe I feel like he's in better hands. There's hope towards the end that things are going to work out for him. But all these wheels have already been set in motion a long time ago.

Interviewer: The rule of inevitability.

Brown: The rule of inevitability. It's got to drop off like ripe fruit in your hand, to be unexpected and inevitable at the same time.

That's what Katherine Anne Porter said, and I believe that. Some readers have a problem accepting that life goes like this sometimes.

Interviewer: I'm intrigued by the sheriff—that scene towards the end of *Joe*. The sheriff comes in as the voice of sanity and says, "You can't take your dog into somebody else's house and let them kill another dog. Joe, you just can't do things like this." Joe's wife tells him, "I can't have a social life because you'd go out and beat the guy up." And he says "Me? Me, do that?" At that point in the novel, which is towards the beginning, you don't really know if in fact he's capable of it. But you find out yeah, he probably would do something like that. The sheriff's a guy who's been wild in the past and he's straightened around. You're not curious about a character like that? I think his story would be interesting.

Brown: He's the last voice of reason trying to speak to Joe. He's already witnessed Joe's descent into the place he got to when he had to fight with all the police officers uptown. He knows full well what is going to happen. He's got his ear on what's going on in the county. He knows Willie shot Joe. He knows what's coming. He says, "How long do you think you and Willie Russell can keep shooting at each other before one of you winds up dead?" Joe just laughs and says, "Huh, somebody ought to do the world a favor." That's what he means, too. The world would be better off if that son of a bitch was dead.

Interviewer: He's right. But the sheriff knows something that Joe doesn't know about reality.

Brown: And the sheriff has to operate on the right side of the law, but Joe doesn't. There's nobody to take care of it but Joe. It just

> *"A person goes through learning to write just like a brick mason learns how to lay an even course."*

---

falls into his lap. If somebody doesn't take care of these people right now—Willie and Wade—this is going to happen again, and no telling how long it's been happening. They stole Gary's truck, Willie's beaten him up, now his dad's selling his little sister, took his money. How much more am I going to let him get away with? That's Joe's question.

Interviewer: You still haven't answered my question about writing a novel from the point of view of these members of the community.

Brown: The novel I'm working on now is about a guy, Glen, getting out of the penitentiary after three years, and coming home. I was pretty sure that this novel was going to focus on him. But he gets met at the cemetery—his mother has died while he's in the pen—he gets met at the cemetery the first day he's home by the sheriff, a guy that he grew up with. And slowly the focus, as I wrote, began to slide over to Bobby, the sheriff, and his home life. Bobby is a really good man. He's that voice of reason in the book I'm working on now. But these two characters have something between them, and that is they both want the same woman. She has had Glen's illegitimate child before he went in, so the child is between three and four years old now. But in the three years he's been down, the sheriff has been out and she's been unattached. They haven't actually been lovers, but they've gotten to feeling very, very strongly about each other, and she's going to give Glen one chance to come back, claim this baby and give it a name. She's still unmarried. Bobby wants her. He's willing to take the baby too, give it his name, do everything. All he wants is a family. He wants them for his family. Glen doesn't really care if he ever has a family or not because he's very estranged from his own family, from his father, from things

---

"You walk a fine line between weeping over stuff and turning a cold eye to it."

that have gone before. He has a lot of hatred. He blames a lot of people for the mistakes that he's made. The one thing that he's going to do when he comes home is take care of his enemies. He begins to do that as soon as he gets home.

Interviewer: A lot of people who study the lives of policemen say that they have difficulty in their personal lives because their world vision gets skewed from what they're seeing all the time. In reading *On Fire* I couldn't help but wonder if you think that all those years you spent on the Oxford Fire Department intensified that attention to the darker side. You talk in there about how mainly in your work you see people over and over again that have been out driving drunk, decapitated on bridges, young lives snuffed out, people burned to death from doing something totally stupid like driving while drunk, people who get drunk and burn the apartment down. Was it just a good source of material, or do you think in fact it shaped your view of the world?

Brown: What it showed me was that poverty causes many of these terrible tragedies, because the people who are on the lower end of the economic scale are the ones who have the lousy housing, who live in the firetraps. Why? Because the wiring is bad, because somebody's been careless, somebody's put a penny in the fuse box and there's a wire under the rug, or the smoke detector doesn't have a battery in it, or their child has never been told not to play with matches and catches the curtains on fire, then catches their pajamas on fire. Of course, it can happen to anybody. Some fellow can go out and have a car wreck in his big Cadillac. But so many times you may go from the biggest mansion in the city of Oxford that morning down to the most squalid shack on the other side of town that evening. You can figure which one's going to be the worst. It's because of the conditions that poor people live in. You get your eyes opened to something like that, and it makes you appreciate the life that you have, and the things that you've been taught, and your children. Even though they might get a little wild sometimes, at least they're not out selling drugs or robbing folks on the street. It also tends to make you appreciate family even more. Many of the things that I saw in the Fire Department were so bad, and the memories of them wouldn't let me sleep sometimes. All that stuff is what I write about—what I saw and the way it made me feel.

Interviewer: Everybody who talks to Larry Brown hears that when he was twenty-nine he decided to start writing. But somehow there's got to be more to it. What happened? You'd been on the Fire Department seven years at this point. You were married. You had at least two or three of your children.

Brown: Right before I turned thirty I looked at my life and I said, "Okay, what are you going to do with it?" I think I just wanted to make something more out of myself than what I was. Being a firefighter was, and is, I still think, a very noble, honorable profession because it's in the business of helping people. But I said, "Isn't there something else you can do with your life that might be even better?" I said, "Well, what about writing?" As much as I loved to read, I wanted to know how people went into a room and sat down and created a book out of their imagination or memory or whatever—created this book where nothing had existed before, a tangible object you could pick up and hold in your hand. How did people do that? I decided, "All it's going to cost is a typewriter and paper, a very basic thing. I'm going to write a novel."

Interviewer: It could have also cost your family life, your personal life, as you illustrate so well in some of your stories about writers.

Brown: For many years nobody understood what I was doing or why I was doing it. I'd had a project not too long before that where I was going to disassemble a '55 Chevrolet and put it back together. I had it up on blocks in my pasture. The whole thing lay in pieces and never got put back together. Somebody finally came and towed it away. Mary Annie probably thought writing was just another little whim like that. But a couple of years later I was still working hard at it. She began to see that I was dedicating myself to changing careers, to stopping the job as a firefighter to become a writer. I think the years that a person goes through learning to write are just like the years that a journeyman carpenter goes through, or a brick mason goes through, learning how to lay an even course. It's an acquired skill. I don't think people are born with talent. The reason I say that is because if you went out to the house and climbed up in the attic and looked at all those bad novels and stories that are up there gathering dust, you would say that Larry Brown has no talent. You would have to.

Interviewer: That's interesting, because I know people who after twenty years think of themselves as aspiring writers and the stuff they're writing is still bad. I guess it's a question of learning from your mistakes. How did you identify the mistakes in the first place, to learn from them? Writing is so solitary. You don't have a steward over you saying, "You didn't tie that knot right. Here's how you do that."

Brown: One thing you have to do is lose all your sentimental feelings about your characters. You also have to get a certain

"Many people's lives are not right and are never going to be right."

amount of bullshit out of your system to tell what's genuine from what's fake. There are two ways you can go. You can be sentimental, or you can be hard-hearted. The perfect place to be is right in the middle. You walk a fine line between weeping over the stuff and turning a cold eye on it. You can't fool people. You have to be honest with them. I think that you go into a room and you believe in yourself. You must have this unshakeable belief, no matter if you can prove it today or not, that you're going to make it. That's the only thing that kept me going. I told myself, "If I do this thing long enough, I will eventually learn how." It takes discipline to actually commit to sit down and do the work, to invent all these hundreds of stories and ideas that you come up with that don't even get finished, that get thrown away. It's mainly up to you. I don't think that I was born with any talent. I think it's more just a way I have of looking at the world that's different from how most people look at the world, but that people everywhere can identify with.

Interviewer: You said you came to Ole Miss to take a writing course from Ellen Douglas. What did that teach you?

Brown: She told me, "I don't have any problem with the way you construct a sentence. It's your subject matter that you need to learn about—what the things are to write about." My first novel was about a man-eating grizzly bear in Yellowstone National Park. The next one was about a couple of guys who were going to raise a big patch of marijuana in Tennessee and sell it. The third novel was a supernatural novel. The fourth was a boxing novel. I don't know anything about boxing. I've watched a lot of it, but I never have done any of it. The fifth novel was about some guys who lived out in the woods around here, and it almost got published.

"I wanted to say something about the people who make these sacrifices for us."

Then I started writing *Joe* and *Dirty Work*, and I published both of them.

Interviewer: You took six years to write *Joe*. How long did you take to write *Dirty Work*?

Brown: I wrote *Dirty Work* in two and a half years of very hard work. I didn't do anything else for those two and a half years.

Interviewer: What started that?

Brown: I took six months off from writing in 1986 to build the house that I live in now. *Joe* was already underway, but I said, "Okay, I can't go drive nails for twelve hours and then write at night, too, so I'm just going to drop it for six months, get the house built and move in it. Then I'll start back writing again." During the time that the house was under construction, I got an idea about a guy whose face was disfigured from a rocket attack in Vietnam and he wouldn't come out of his room. That was all I had. It was just driving me crazy to get to work on it, but I couldn't until I had all the sheetrock hung, and the wallpaper and paint, trim, the cabinets, all the million things that go in a house. But the day that I had a table to put my typewriter on, and a chair to sit in—we hadn't even moved in yet—I sat down and started writing *Dirty Work*. That idea had grown and festered in those months and I just had to get it down. It turned out that I had to write it five different times and throw out six hundred pages. It went through five complete revisions.

Interviewer: At what point did the two voices come in, of Walter and Braiden?

Brown: After the third draft, when I finally showed the manuscript to my editor, Shannon Ravenel. She wrote back and said, "Larry, the bad news is your novel starts on page 160." I said, "Oh, no. That's unacceptable. I'm just going to throw it away. I've put in too much work. I'm not going to go through all that." She wrote me a letter and said, "You have worked by yourself all this time. You haven't had any guidance, I understand all of that. But this is too good an idea for you to throw away. Just trust me and work on it with me. I'm going to help you." And she was right. We started working on it again. I started writing the fourth draft. We sent things back and forth. We'd argue sometimes. We'd have our disagreements. But in the process I discovered that she was right about all that stuff. She was the one who taught me so much about characters' histories, their relationships, their feelings, their memories, their childhoods, their concerns, and how characters had to be so well fleshed out.

Interviewer: To what extent do you accept or are you comfortable with *Dirty Work*'s identification as a novel of the Vietnam era, and of you as a novelist of the Vietnam era?

Brown: The word *Vietnam* is never mentioned in that book. It's about the aftermath of the war more than the war itself. There aren't a whole lot of combat scenes. There's a little bit about the war in there. But it's mainly about what happens to people years and years on down the road. That's why it carries the dedication that it does: "This book is for Daddy, who knew what war does to men." He saw and went through so many terrible things. The guys that I met did too. I wanted to say something about the people who make these sacrifices for us, the veterans—the guys who we honor every Memorial Day. Sometimes what happens to them is not pretty. Many people's lives are not right, and are never going to be right. Those are the people I explore over and over. If you don't have problems in your characters' lives, then you don't have a story. The way to hook your reader is to give your character some trouble early on, and then find out what's going to happen, and sandbag him and put all this pressure on him and see how he's going to react when things really get tough.

Interviewer: *Dirty Work* also seems to me to be a book that's about the question of how God works in this world. There's a real dialogue that's taking place at a philosophical and a spiritual level between Walter and Braiden throughout the book. Were you conscious of that as being one of the questions you wanted to address?

Brown: Certainly. I wanted to address what I felt God would say about Braiden, the situation that he's in, having lived for twenty years without arms or legs. He's reached a point where he just wants to die, but he has to persuade someone to do that for him. Jesus comes down and explains everything very straightforwardly to him: "I can't take your life. This guy over here, that's something else, but you're treading on shaky ground." It's not exactly suicide, but in a way it kind of is, too. But I also believe that God is very merciful and compassionate, and would not blame Braiden for wanting to leave, even though life is what he gave you— "all of us," that's what he says. That's very much true. Life is what he gave us. But some lives get to the point where they're unbearable, and Braiden's life has gotten to that point.

Interviewer: Braiden says at one point about the question of suffering in the world, "God doesn't work like that. God doesn't

"I was trying to create a situation that most people would never encounter."

---

visit suffering on the world. Things just get out of hand." So what do you think, philosophically? Is Braiden speaking for you?

Brown: I don't know if he's speaking for me. I've got a very deep faith. I'm not a compulsive churchgoer. I was for many, many years. I was raised in a church. I don't go like I used to, but I still have this faith. I believe that the world is a hard place for a lot of people, but there are also many, many good things about it. You hardly ever hear about the good things. I think in some ways I was trying to create a situation that most people would never encounter, but I wanted those people to know what Braiden had been going through and what a good human being he was, and what the loss of him was. We lost a schoolteacher, we lost some guy who was going to try and help other people with his life. He was really a kid, and then he lost everything that he had. The world's forgotten about him. All the medals have been pinned on and the TV's turned to another channel. He's still here, and he's going to be here unless somebody can do something for him.

Interviewer: You've talked quite a bit about the struggle you went through to establish yourself as a writer. How do you feel about it now that you have published five books?

Brown: Many times it's still a complete shock to me to just see a finished book and say, "How did you ever manage to accomplish that?" But it's an accumulation of time. You spend every day doing it, and you spend enough days together in a row, then you've got a book. It's like building a house. It may be real hard—the days may be real hot or real cold when you're doing it—but after the house is finished, no matter how tired your muscles have been

---

"Spend enough days together in a row, then you've got a book. It's like building a house."

on all those other days, the memory of the work is something that goes away. You're left with the finished product.

"Hey — I'm between books. You're between books. What better time to get married."

Saml L. Clemens

Col. Sellers
A Drama
In
Five Acts
by
Saml L. Clemens
"Mark Twain"
Elmira, N. Y.

Entered in the Office of the Librarian of Congress July 1874

Cast of Characters

Col. Mulberry Sellers—

Si Hawkins—

Clay Hawkins—his adopted son

Lafayette Hawkins—son of Si Hawkins

Col. George Selby—an ex Rebel—

Judge of Court—

Prosecuting Attorney—

Duffer—Counsel for the defense—

Uncle Daniel—an old stammering Negro—

John Peterson—a servant—

Mrs Si Hawkins—

Emily Hawkins—Her Daughter—

Laura Hawkins—Her adopted Daughter—

Mrs Mulberry Sellers—

Jury. Sheriff. Messengers—

Servants—Citizens & c & c

COLONEL SELLERS / *Saml L. Clemens*

Introduction

Nineteenth-century American literature is not known for its drama. Yet the theatre, as popular entertainment, was widely regarded as a quintessentially democratic forum. Traveling players performed on riverboats, in boom towns and mining camps and in the multitude of "opera houses" scattered throughout the country. After the Civil War, improved rail transportation made such performances readily available to an ever-growing populace in the West. Productions of Shakespeare and adaptations of German and French plays were commonplace, but dramatizations of American works such as *Rip Van Winkle* and *Uncle Tom's Cabin* also had long and profitable runs. It is in this context that authors such as Henry James, William Dean Howells, Bret Harte, Mark Twain, and many others wanted to succeed in the drama as well as in fiction. Provided one might produce a play of long-standing appeal, there was money and celebrity to be had.

Mark Twain's involvement in the drama was long-standing and, for the most part, ill-fated. He had written drama criticism for the Virginia City *Territorial Enterprise* as early as 1862, and over the course of his career wrote, either alone or in collaboration, over twenty plays; he translated into English three German plays and supervised the dramatization of six of his novels. Only the play *Colonel Sellers*, now published for the first time, can be considered a true success, however.

The genesis and history of its production are fascinating and intricate stories in themselves. In February 1874, Twain reported that he had written a "queer play," possibly one based on the novel *The Gilded Age*, which he and Charles Dudley Warner had written and to which the figure of Sellers was Twain's most interesting contribution. Whatever Twain's dramatic aspirations may have been at the time, however, when he heard that a production of the play based on the novel and dramatized by G.B. Densmore was planned in San Francisco, he took immediate action. He wrote to Warner that he knew Densmore well enough and resolved that "he shan't run any play on MY brains."

By May, Twain had enjoined the Densmore play against future performances and written or rewritten his own. He finished *Colonel Sellers* by July 15, 1874, presumably having John Raymond, who had been in the Densmore production, in mind to play the title role. Twain bought the Densmore script for $200, promising to pay another $200 if his own play proved successful. On July 20, Twain submitted an amanuensis copy of his play for copyright, and he wrote Robert Mackenzie that he was well enough satisfied with his rendering of Sellers: "I meant him to be at all times & under all circumstances a *gentleman* & so he is, now....I am very glad you like the old speculator (he still lives, & is drawn from life, not imagination)—I ate a turnip dinner with him years ago."

But whatever may have been Twain's artistic ambition, it eventually vied with another intention—that the play should make money. As it turned out, *Colonel Sellers* was one of the most prosperous children of Twain's fertile imagination. From its opening night in 1874 until its final performance twelve years later, *Colonel Sellers* was a perennial success and eventually earned Twain well over $100,000, more than he made from the sales of either *Huckleberry Finn* or *Tom Sawyer*. Nevertheless, Twain felt that Raymond played the Colonel too much as a comic and slightly preposterous visionary and never really understood the nature of the role: "I threw all my strength into the character of Colonel Sellers," Twain remarked in a speech reprinted in the *New York World*, "hoping to make it a very strong tragedy part, and pathetic. [Raymond] *tries* hard to play it right and make it majestic and pathetic; but his *face* is against him....Oh! I can see that he tries hard to make it solemn and awful and heroic, but really sometimes he almost makes me laugh."

The basis for the popularity of *Colonel Sellers* was, however, its comedy, not its pathos. Though Twain resented this fact, he was not willing to forgo the profits from the play. Rather he chose to distance himself from the play and Raymond. In later years, after Raymond's death and the cessation of production, Twain again remembered the fondness he had held for the Colonel. In his *Autobiography* he wrote, "The real Colonel Sellers was never on the stage. Only half of him was there. Raymond could not play the other half of him; it was above his level." But the performer and audience may have been a step ahead of the writer in this instance. Colonel Sellers is a classic comic character, sharing more with Charlie Chaplin's Tramp than with any of the possible tragic models. He is resilient in his poverty, blithe yet creative—a classic example of innate grace shining through foolishness.

Note: The most comprehensive published work on Twain as dramatist is Thomas Schirer's *Mark Twain and the Theatre* (Nurnberg, 1984), but see also Robert Goldman, "Mark Twain as Playwright" in *Mark Twain: A Sumptuous Variety*, edited by Edward Giddings (Barnes and Noble, 1985). The fullest treatment of *Colonel Sellers* is Jerry Thomason's "Colonel Sellers: The Story of a Play," Ph.D. diss. U. of Missouri, 1991. The text published here is derived from the edition of the play Thomason prepared.

Jerry Thomason
Tom Quirk

Saml L. Clemens

Act 1st = *Scene 1st Mississippi River* = *Set Waters & Stage* Enter Mr & Mrs Hawkins *Bank R. 1.E*

Hawkins: Well, Nancy, old Wife, we're far enough from Tennessee now. You're satisfied my Wife?

Mrs Hawkins: Any place that suits my husband suits me—Si Hawkins, and the children?

Hawkins: [Interrupting her] O, the Children, will be *better* off—I've looked after them. Nancy, do you see these papers? [Displaying papers] Well they're evidence that I've taken up seventy five thousand acres of land in Tennessee. Took them up a month before we left. Think what an enormous fortune it will be some day—Why *enormous* don't express it! Nancy—The word's too tame! [Loud] I tell you Nancy—

Mrs Hawkins: For goodness sake Si—Sh—Sh—

Hawkins: [Taking her by the arm & leading her to the front] Sh—Sh—I want to tell you Nancy—

Mrs Hawkins: [Eagerly] Go on Si. You can trust me.

Hawkins: [Cautiously] Now all that's necessary to keep this land in the family, is to pay the trifling taxes on it yearly—say five or ten dollars—The whole tract wouldn't fetch more than a third of a cent an acre now; but some day people will be glad to get it for twenty dollars—fifty dollars—a hundred dollars an acre! What would you say—[Drops his voice & looks around] to a thousand dollars an acre?

Mrs Hawkins: Oh, Si, Si. A thousand dollars an acre?

Hawkins: Yes! And that ain't all, there's coal on our land, worlds of coal—

Mrs Hawkins: Oh, Si. It makes me dizzy to hear you!

Hawkins: And that ain't all neither! There's Iron, Nancy, a whole mountain of iron on our land. You just wait till the Rail Roads & the Steam Boat's come—You'll see! or rather they'll see. That's the main point. Why Nancy, they'll ride in their coaches, they'll live like princes of the earth, they'll be courted & worshiped, perhaps we'll have to drag along in toil & poverty. Ah—well-a-day! Will they ever come to our old home & say, "this little spot shall not be touched; this at least shall be sacred; for here our Father & our Mother toiled for us & fought for us & laid the foundations of our future as enduring as the hills"—

Mrs Hawkins: You're a great, good, noble soul, Si—Hawkins, and I'm an honored Woman in being the Wife of such a man—You were out of your place among those groping dumb creatures of East—

Tennessee—I'd rather my body should starve & die than your mind should hunger & wither away in that lonely land!

Hawkins: Spoken like yourself, my child! But we'll not starve yet. O, no. I've strong hopes that our old friend Mulberry Sellers has invested judiciously for us here. Mulberry Sellers—would be a rich man, Nancy, if he wouldn't continually chase after every *Ignus Fatous* that comes along.

[Enter Uncle Dan'l with two children]

Mrs Hawkins: Ignus which?

Hawkins: *Ignus Fatous.*

Mrs Hawkins: [Irritated] Si Hawkins, what is that?

Hawkins: Why, an Ignus Fatous is a "Jack O'Lantern" a "will o' the wisp"—anything that you're always following & never can catch.

Mrs Hawkins: O, that's it, is it? Why didn't you say so at first? Well I don't complain, I guess—Fatous is a good word, a nice, big, wholesome word—

Uncle Dan'l: [Stammering] Mars Hawkins, here comes Mars Sellers.

Hawkins: Where?

Uncle Dan'l: Heah he comes, right heah.

Sellers: Why, Si, old boy how are you. [Shakes hands then turns to Mrs H.] Why Nancy how do do. Well I'm glad to see you. Why what'll my wife say—

Mr & Mrs H.: [Simultaneously] Your Wife?

Sellers: O Yes. I'm married, married last week—O, Nancy you'll like her. You'll love her—You'll be twins, she's the noblest woman that ever walked—It's only this morning, she said to me Colonel, she always will call me Colonel, in spite of anything I can say or do. Colonel she says, I feel that somebody's coming, and here you are—now do you know, she believes she's a prophetess & I believe she is too, there's no country but what a prophet's an honor to as the old proverb says—Let's shake—hands again—

Hawkins: You're the same splendid old heart you always were.

Sellers: Me? Mulberry Sellers, never changes—as Senator Dilworthy said to me this morning—[Sees Uncle Dan'l & children] Why, Lafayette, my boy, how are you? Emily give me a kiss; Bless your souls. You jolly little immigrants, won't I make it lively for you! Well, Uncle Daniel, how *are* you? Black as ever ain't you? But where's Laura, where's Clay?

Hawkins: O, they'll be here soon, strolling around somewhere I suppose, but I say old friend, what's the business prospect?

Sellers: Business prospects? Simply glorious. A Million a year's a small sum to make in this country, but we'll say a million the first year—

Mrs Hawkins: Now, Col. Sellers, isn't that—isn't that—

Sellers: Large? Yes, for Tennessee, but not for Missouri—A million, a paltry million. I'll tell you, how you're to make it. [Mr & Mrs H. gather around him]

Hawkins: How?

Sellers: Mules!

Mrs Hawkins: Mules?

Hawkins: Mules?

Sellers: Mules! Mules, cost nothing here, it costs nothing to keep them, in New Orleans they sell for a hundred dollars a piece.

Hawkins: Why I should think there would be lots of folks go into a business like that!

Sellers: Ah, it's the idea that's wanting, it's the idea! Now this is in strict confidence, we'll go into this thing together.

Hawkins: How much capital will we want?

Sellers: Nothing! A mere trifle, ten thousand dollars, I'll fix that. I've invested a thousand of your money in Mules already—[Mrs H: O, I begin to tremble]. I was going to put the whole of it in, when by the merest accident I thought of a better thing.

Hawkins: Bless my life man, what *can* be a better thing—

Sellers: O, pshaw! Mules are all well enough for a side speculation, but when a man wishes to invest his money in this country, he thinks of something of consequence, so I took your money in my hand & cast a wary eye around; says I, here's the card to put Si Hawkins' money on, & I invested it all in a Steam Boat—

Hawkins: Good heavens!

Mrs Hawkins: Why if it should sink, or burn, or blow *up*, we're just about ruined.

Sellers: Nancy, don't you worry. Your husband owns one sixth of a bran new Steam Boat, "There's millions in it"—millions in it! I wouldn't take three millions for his chances in the Steamer Amaranth for the next five years—

Hawkins: The Amaranth? Why that's the new boat that's coming here to-day—

Sellers: That's the one, I've invested all my capital in it—a nest egg for a National Bank—I'll make more money out of that steamer than any speculation I've gone into for years—[Enter boy] Jerry you want your money, don't you? You shall have it my boy. [Fumbles around in his pockets] [Aside-I've got on my other pants.] Si, lend me ten cents. [Hawkins hands him a dime] There you are my boy, run along. Now as soon as that steamer arrives I'm going to walk on board, says I, Captain what's the state of your finances? & I'll bet you, I come off with a large share of dividend—but come Nancy—come over to the house & see Polly, she'll be expecting you, you glorify no hearth in this country but mine—tuck yourself under my wing. [Puts her arm in his] Dan'l, you bring along the children—

Hawkins: I don't care if I do take a look at your home, home is not an *"Ignus Fatous"* anyhow—I was just telling Nancy, that you'd get rich Mulberry, if you'd only stop chasing after every *"Ignus Fatous"* that comes along—

Sellers: Si, that's no way to talk to me, you ought to know better. I'm too old a man.

Hawkins: Why, Colonel, you misunderstand me.

Sellers: No, I don't, I understand perfectly—well what you mean, but I don't like to be spoken to like that, for I'll *swear* I've never heard the woman's name before. [Exit Mrs H. & Sellers]

Hawkins: Ha! Ha! Ha! Well Dan'l you take care of the children while I go with the Col. & see how the land lies. Laws what a man he is, one day he's rolling in luxury & then again you couldn't ask a blessing over his table without seeming to be sarcastic—[Exit Hawkins].

Uncle Dan'l: Now Chil'en, you mind, & just behave yousef. You's in a strange country now, & if you should go out'en dis he'ah camp, dey's Lions & Elephants, & different kinds of debbils roun he'ah, dat would take & snake the head off'n you, fo' you could spread you'sef & holler—[Noise of Steam Boat whistle. Dan'l jumps back] Good Lawd Chil'len What is dat?

Children: What is it Uncle Daniel?

Uncle Dan'l: Chil'len there's sum'fin a' com'in—

Children: What it is? Oh what is it, Uncle Dan'l?

Uncle Dan'l: It's the debbil chil'len, sure. [Children nestle close to Dan'l] You stick right clos' to me, don't be afeared, I'se wid you. I isn't skeered, I seed him once before up in Tennessee when most folks would have been scared & run but I isn't one of dat kind. I just straightens my'sef up, says I, what do you want heah, says he, I want you. Well Chil'len I had a big club in my hand & I commences to inch up to that air debbil, till I got just so close that I knowed he couldn't skip ou'ten de way—then I ris up so—[Noise of Steam boat again, Dan'l & Children run off the stage]. [Enter Clay & Laura]

Clay: Well, that's the worst case of scare I ever saw. The old man's afraid of the Steam Boat. Here Uncle Dan'l, you rascal, come here. Were you afraid of the Steam Boat? [Enter Uncle Dan'l & Children]

Uncle Dan'l: How can you talk dat way to me Mars Clay, I isn't fraid o' nothin.

Clay: O, you're not, well don't you know any better than to wander out here with my little sister & run the chances of having her eaten up, by an elephant or—

Uncle Dan'l: Why bless your heart Mars Clay wasn't I wid de dear chile?

Clay: O, I forgot that!

Uncle Dan'l: I should tink you did forgot sum'fin. [Exit Dan'l with children]

Clay: Now Laura, why won't you say yes, why won't you consent?

Laura: What a dear old tease you are All these weeks & weeks & months, you do keep at a body so!

Clay: Because I love you Laura, and I can't help it—indeed I don't *want* to help it—

Laura: Well, you know I *love you* too—as a brother.

Clay: I know that; but that's not it! Laura Hawkins, you know we're not brother and sister, although we *are* adopted by the same family. Ever since I was ten years of age, I've known no Father & Mother but Mr. & Mrs. Hawkins, and they *seem* like Father & Mother to me, and you seemed a sister to me long ago, when they found you, a parentless & friendless little child, and added you to their family in their noble, unselfish way; but there's no blood of ours in their veins—there's no blood of yours in mine—and now for a *long* time Laura, ever since I have been of age—you have become a thousand times dearer to me than any sister! Can't you love me a little more, just a little more than as a brother? You know how it would please father & mother.

Laura: I do, indeed, I do—and they've been so loving and so generous to me.

Clay: Their hearts are set on this one desire—bound up in it Laura!

Laura: I know it—I know it so well—and it makes me feel wicked and ungrateful, when I look into my heart, and find day after day, hard as I may try, that I am still only loving you as a brother, and yet after all that they have done for me, I would do anything in this world to gratify their least little wish—Clay, your nature is just as beautiful as any that ever adorned a human creature, but—

Clay: Still you cannot love me?

Laura: Oh! don't say that Clay. I do love you. I cannot tell how *deeply* & *warmly* I love you, but I fear—I cannot *help* fearing, that it is only sisterly love after all—

Clay: It is hard—very hard—[after a pause]. Well, Laura, I shall not stop here, in the new house we have all journeyed to—I shall go farther—

Laura: [With interest & concern] Why, Clay, you cannot mean it, where are you going—

Clay: O, Somewhere—anywhere—but you will not mind it—

Laura: Oh Clay. [With a disturbed look] You surely cannot mean that, I can't have you go away. Father's not rich, but he's not poor; he loves you with all his heart. Why seek your fortune among strangers—

Clay: It isn't that. I'm seeking life. I can't tear you out of my heart, while you are still before my eyes. I wanted to make one more attempt in this last interview. I have thought of it for a long time—it will almost kill me to go away from you—

Laura: Oh! I do not know what to do, for I do not know my own heart. I dare not say the words for fear—[After reflection]. Clay!

Clay: Yes Laura!

Laura: Give me time—Give me time to learn my own heart—then you shall know—

Clay: All the time you wish Laura.

Laura: You shall go away as you have said, I'll give you an answer, but we'll set no date. Let me have time to consider then you shall know. Please look cheerful Clay. I don't want to give you pain, and I'm trying not to.

Clay: Thank you a thousand times for such pain Laura; there's healing for it in the hope it brings—[Enter Sellers with Mr & Mrs Hawkins].

Sellers: That property will be worth three millions in two years—[Sees Clay & Laura]. Why Clay my boy, how are you. [Shakes hands] Miss Laura—how do do, I'm delighted to see you—but I must talk with the old folks. Now Nancy when I was a young man I used to have my ideas, but—experience teaches a man, now I never touch anything, without having first weighed it in my judgement, and when Mulberry Sellers, puts his judgement on a thing, *there it is*.

Mrs H.: [Aside] What a man he is to talk, and he believes every word he says—And so that persuades nine people out of ten to believe him too.

Hawkins: What is this about—Stone Landing?

Sellers: Stone Landing? That's Napoleon, you couldn't get an appropriation for Stone Landing, the name would kill it, and Goose Run, that's Columbia River, on the new map—

Hawkins: So you're after an appropriation are you?

Sellers: After an appropriation? The first thing you know, the appropriation will be after us; Congress never had such an opportunity to distinguish itself, it will *jump* at it. The *President* will jump at it—all the nations of the earth will jump to locate in Napoleon, all you've got to do is to calculate how much money you want, sit down and rake it in—

Hawkins: But about this appropriation. Whose going to engineer the bill through Congress?

Sellers: Who? Why, my friend Senator Dilworthy! Ah, he's a great man & a noble man, & a *good* man too—Well, a man *has* to be good to succeed in these days. Now he's only been in Congress a few years and *he's* worth a million—

Mrs Hawkins: Well! We live to learn. I've always been taught that goodness was mighty poor truck to get rich on—

Sellers: That was in the olden times Nancy, things have changed now—Why to show you how good Dilworthy is, when he came to stay with me, he said Mulberry, when do you have prayers? Before breakfast or after breakfast? Well I had to speak right out. I had to tell him we didn't have them at all—that is—not steady, he said he understood business interruptions and all that, but for himself, he never forgot the ordinances of religion—he didn't believe Columbia River appropriation would pass if he forgot to invoke divine blessing—[Uncle Dan'l runs from rear of stage].

Uncle Dan'l: Oh! Mars Sellers, what is dis? a whoopin and a tearin down the river—

Sellers: Si! There's a Steam Boat race! There's something to amuse you. [Small Boat is seen crossing rear of stage] There's the Boreas— & there comes the Amaranth! [Large Boat approaches] I'm going on board of her—[Explosion of large Boat]—[Bustle & confusion].

Tableau and Curtain

Act 2nd Scene 1st

A lapse of nine years is supposed to have occurred. A room in Hawkins' house at Hawkeye poorly furnished—Hawkins discovered.

Hawkins: Over nine years since we left Tennessee. We've had our ups and downs—but the downs have got the advantage now. The Steam Boat calamity nearly sent us to the poor house, but the Mules set us on our feet again. Then Seller's sugar speculation fetched us down once more. We made money in a tannery, & sunk it again in a perpetual motion machine, invented by Sellers—Poor Sellers means well, but—well, just as he got the Columbia River appropriation under way, along come the war & stops everything. But thank heaven, the Tennessee land is safe—the *children* will be rich, even if we die poor. In the blackest days—I've been sorely tempted to sell it, when I had big offers, but I've always had the strength given me to refuse at the last moment—But to tell the truth, times are blacker *now* than ever before—[Enter Mrs Hawkins].

Mrs Hawkins: Si, I don't know what we are going to do. Fanny and Georgie and Franky are not fit to be seen, their clothes are in such a state—But there's something more serious still—We've scarcely a bite in the house to eat—

Hawkins: Why Nancy, go to Johnson—

Mrs Hawkins: Johnson indeed! And you saved that man from beggary twice! He told Franky this morning that our bill was running pretty high & turned him away without giving him the meat he went for.

Hawkins: Why Nancy! Is it so bad as this? This is astounding

Mrs Hawkins: And so it is—I warrant you—I've kept still, Si, as long as ever I could, but things are getting worse & worse and I don't know what in the world to do. [Buries her face in her hands]

Hawkins: [Caressing her] Poor child, don't grieve so. I am *ashamed* of myself! But you shan't suffer another day—not another day. I'll sell the *land!* If I can find a purchaser at *any price.*

Mrs Hawkins: [Excitedly] Would you sell it, Si?

Hawkins: This instant!

Mrs Hawkins: Oh! We're saved! I'll find the purchaser.

Hawkins: Are you serious?

Mrs Hawkins: Indeed I am!

Hawkins: How *can* a man lose faith? When the darkest hour comes, Providence always comes with it. Quick, Nancy, where is he?

Mrs Hawkins: Waiting in the best room.

Hawkins: He shan't wait long. [Exit]

Mrs Hawkins: [Sits] [Soliloquizing] But I've small confidence now— What shall we do? If Laura had only married Clay years ago, but no, something broke it off of course—just like the most of our luck some how. And now she and Emily are tied here in this miserable hovel. Poor Laura, beautiful, proud, high-spirited—how this poverty chafes her! And I don't like that Colonel Selby, that talks to her as if she was a queen—It's enough to turn any poor girl's head; and he isn't the man to marry a girl out of his station in life—What *will* become of us?—[Enter Laura now aged 25 and Emily aged 17].

Laura: Mother, what is the matter?

Mrs Hawkins: You know, Laura. It's hard times—hard times. Your father's got a chance to sell the land, now, but—well, whatever's offered, he'll ask more—he always does—he'll never sell. Heaven seems to have deserted us.

Laura: Then the more need that we should help ourselves—

Mrs Hawkins: What can we do?

Laura: I will go to St Louis—There will be one mouth less to feed.

Mrs Hawkins: What can you do in St Louis?

Laura: I will find something to do, I will work.

Mrs Hawkins: Never Laura—We are good southern blood, and our daughters cannot work for a living—No, we will live or die together.

Laura: Ah, mother keep heart—we shall *live* together, not die— [Emily then kneels by her Mother].

Emily: Let us do something, Mamma—Laura and I can go together and take care of each other.

Mrs Hawkins: [Putting her arms around Emily's neck] No, no, my Child—There's human wolves enough around here, without sending you to the big City.

Laura: [Giving a start & glancing at Mrs Hawkins] Human wolves, Mother? What do you mean?

Mrs Hawkins: I mean men that court girls they don't mean to marry.

Laura: [Biting her lips. Showing signs of indignation—She approaches Mrs Hawkins.] Do you mean Col. Selby?

Mrs Hawkins: Don't be angry, Laura—I speak for your good—I don't like to have Col. Selby here so much—I do *plead* with you to tell him not to come any more.

Laura: Mother, since it grieves you so—I—I *will* tell him.

Mrs Hawkins: Thank you a hundred times, my Child. I don't say that he means anything bad. These men never do mean bad; but they do a heap of mischief.

Laura: I'll ask him not to come any more. But it's very lonely here, and he's the only real Gentleman in Hawkeye—

Mrs Hawkins: If he *is* a real Gentleman, Laura, he won't be offended. Gentlemen know poor girls must protect their good name. It'll be so much better for us all, if he don't come any more. I want to thank you again, my darling, [approaching and kissing Laura] and now I'll go and see if your father has done anything. [Exit]

Emily: [Putting her arms around Laura] Do you care so much, Laura?

Laura: Care? Who is there here, that can compare with Col. Selby?

Emily: No one, perhaps; but Mamma is right—he does not belong to our world.

Laura: Then Emily, we must fit ourselves for his. The life we are leading now, is mere vegetation—we don't *live* we only exist.

Emily: [Laura sits] Laura, what a girl you are! You're as ambitious as—now Laura what can Col. Selby do for you more than another might?

Laura: Girl! I am a *woman* now! My love for Col. Selby has made a *woman* of me, Child! What can he do for me? He can take me out into that great mysterious world I dream of—where there is *action!—action!* I want to *do* something. I want to *be* something. I won't *be* a silly, trashy, village inanity, to simper my useless life out and then pass away like the weeds—only enriching the earth by becoming a *part* of it.

Emily: Hity-tity—I've ambitions too, but—

Laura: But they're not gunpowder and brimstone ones! Is that it little Sister?

Emily: Yes. I don't want any *pow-wow* and all that sort of thing. Now I'd like to have a nice quiet *good* natured husband, who'd love me, and pet me, and give me nice clothes—not *gaudy*, you know, but *nice*, and heaps of them. O I'd like to have a nice new dress every four or five months!

Laura: It's a nice, domestic, pretty little ambition child—and the husband who would mar it, would be a wretch—

Emily: Oh! No, he wouldn't be *that*, Laura, not so bad as *that*. But still if he *could* dress me like that—and give me a gold ring—O a *real* gold ring Laura!—

Laura: Then you would be the happiest little creature—

Emily: In the whole world, Laura, and then if we could have ever so many nice good books to read, and a preacher—that was a *good* preacher—and if we could have pie *every* day—

Laura: Bless us! what a Paradise! If ever I get rich you shall *have* it too—preacher, pies and all. [Kisses her]

Emily: Now Laura, tell me *your* ambition.

Laura: [Earnestly] O it is all vague, vague, vague, only this. I won't be no stick or stone! I want to *help—help—*help every soul that needs it, rich or poor, great or small. I want to do every kind deed that comes in my way to do—I want to make somebody glad I was born, every day that I live. *I* don't care what it is—I'd go and slave in a hospital. I'd *glory* in it. Set Soldiers on their feet again! There's a noble work! It's next to *being* a Soldier! And just think!—to have the gratitude of such men as that—O, a thousand times I've thought of Florence Nightingale moving like a ministering Angel among the wounded soldiers in the Crimean Hospitals, and those grateful heroes, forgetting their sufferings, turning their poor bandaged heads to kiss her shadow as it drifted across their pillows!

Emily: O, did they do that?

Laura: Yes, and with tears in their eyes, too. Ah, and when a man's gratitude comes in tears, it comes clear from the bottom of his heart! [Laura rises]

Emily: Laura, I believe you'd as soon be a Soldier as not.

Laura: To save my Country? With my whole heart I would— What did Joan of Arc do that *I* wouldn't do? *Without* her armor of proof!—*without* her consecrated banners!—*without* her all protecting superstition!—but just as I am [straightening up and marching] I'd follow the drums into battle!—and I'd *rejoice* in the fire and smoke and the thunder of the guns!

Emily: You'd do it! I tell you, you look it.

Laura: Do it! I'd do anything noble in a righteous cause—[Enter Uncle Dan'l].

Uncle Dan'l: Miss Laura—Mars Selby's come—[Emily kisses Laura. Exit].

Laura: Very well—show him in—

Uncle Dan'l: Miss Laura de war's ober, an I'se only a free niggah now, but if you says so I'll tell Mars Selby, you ain't at home. 'Deed I'll tell him—

Laura: But I am at home, you good old impudence. [Aside] Even Uncle Daniel is uneasy! [Exit Dan'l] [Enter Col. Selby a man about Forty (40) handsomely dressed—erect, soldierly bearing— heavy moustache—slight limp—walks with cane. She advances & throws herself into Selby's arms.] Oh, George, George, I am so glad you have come!

Col. Selby: [Looking down in her face—and caressing her] What is it, my pet, has anything happened?

Laura: Nothing *has* happened, but everything *may* happen at any moment.

Col. Selby: Well, we won't hurry events.

Laura: But how much longer is this to last?

Col. Selby: I really don't know.

Laura: [Releasing herself from his embrace] Don't know! One would judge from your tone, that you don't care!

Col. Selby: I *do* care—But I am not yet in a position to do as I would.

Laura: There is something of even more importance, George—than wealth or position.

Col. Selby: Will you please tell me what that something is?

Laura: [Bowing her head] It is a woman's honor.

Col. Selby: [Petulantly] The old story! I'm tired of it!

Laura: And I am tired of repeating it.

Col. Selby: Pray desist then.

Laura: [Indignantly] Desist! Are you speaking to me, George Selby? To me—your—

Col. Selby: Hush, darling! Let us have no scene. Has anything happened?

Laura: That has happened which will separate us, unless—

Col. Selby: [Coldly] Well?

Laura: [In a low tone] We choose *not* to be separated.

Col. Selby: We cannot so choose at this moment. The war has left me a ruined man. I must have time to get on my feet—to gather up the wreck of what remains, and make a home.

Laura: [Softening] A home! Ah, George, a very poor home will do for me, if you are there.

Col. Selby: Possibly—for a time—you look at the present—I at the future.

Laura: The future! Ah, me, how dark it is! [Pause] Though I never see you again, George, you must not come to the house any more. This has been urged—commanded.

Col. Selby: By whom?

Laura: All that have any authority. My brother Clay for one.

Col. Selby: [With a slight start] Is he here? **Laura:** He soon will be. He writes to ask me who Col. Selby is.

Col. Selby: And what will you tell him?

Laura: That Col. Selby, is my—friend.

Col. Selby: You are a good girl, Laura, I trust you implicitly—

Laura: And will you love me?

Col. Selby: [Extending his arms] Love you darling—love you?

Laura: [Sinking into his arms] I am so harassed in mind, George, so disheartened, so full of bodings—My only hope, my refuge is in your love.

Col. Selby: Have patience, and all will yet be well.

Laura: I will try to be patient—But it is so hard to have all my friends regard me with so much uneasiness—may be suspicion.

Col. Selby: I know it. I know it. I am a monster of selfishness. I would give you a dagger if you would plunge it into my heart.

Laura: I *would*, George, if you should cease to love me—

Col. Selby: Would you?

Laura: As sure as—No—No. I wouldn't *now*. But by and by—with the wrong rankling in my heart—No, I hope and pray I never could—Oh! I must not *think* such dreadful things.

Col. Selby: [Embracing her] I would be a villain if I ceased to love you, Laura, I would deserve death!

Laura: But you never will cease to love me, will you George?

Col. Selby: Never.

Laura: I believe you—I trust you with all my heart George.

Col. Selby: Indeed you may—I shall be worthy of it, Laura. I must go now—but I must see you again.

Laura: I—I *cannot* say no. I do not *live* when you are out of my sight—I will see you, three days hence—but not here—you know where—same hour as before—Good bye.

Col. Selby: [Extricating himself] Good bye. [Embraces her] [Exit]

Laura: [Gazing after him] Can it be as Clay says, that he is a man to shun. If so, what will become of me? [Sinks upon a chair] [Enter Mrs Hawkins]

Mrs Hawkins: [Aside] Poor child, I do pity her, with all my heart. [She approaches]

Laura: [Rises with a calm face & smiles] Don't be troubled about me, Mother. Col. Selby will not come to the house any more. [Aside] Oh, since I ventured to enter into one deception in an unguarded hour, how my whole life seems growing into a sham—how deftly I have learned to veneer a rugged lie, with the grace & color of truth!

Mrs Hawkins: [Embracing her] I am so grateful. [Enter Col. Sellers seedy but in high spirits]

Sellers: Morning, Nancy, how dy-do? And Laura! Beauty & grandeur, and spirit—What a queen you do look, my child.

Laura: Now it isn't kind of you to say such pretty things to an old friend in such a covertly, satirical way, Colonel.

Sellers: Covertly, satirical! [Earnestly] Ah my child, if I caught any man making you his target for a satire, he would feel the weight of a hand that falls heavy, when it is lifted in a friend's quarrel.

Laura: Light or heavy. I hope it will never fall on me.

Sellers: Never fear about that little duchess—But I've good news, Nancy, famous news!

Mrs Hawkins: Good news—it's so long since I've heard any.

Sellers: Things have gone a little outrageous—but the sun is breaking, the clouds are going to shine again. No I mean the sun—no matter Senator Dilworthy's here!

Mrs Hawkins: Well, Senator Dilworthy, may be a rich man, and a good man, and a great man, but what can he do for us?

Sellers: Do? Why the appropriation, Nancy—the appropriation. We are going to haul in a couple of hundred thousand, on that mighty soon, now. But that's only to start with. We'll strike for a couple of millions next year, that's the way Dilworthy puts up the programme, and he knows—

Laura: Do you expect to get an appropriation Col. Sellers—you a confederate soldier?

Sellers: Bless you, my dear child. I'm reconstructed—I accept the situation. I held out as long as the last one. But now I say let bygones be bygones. I'm reconstructed and I go in for the old flag, and an appropriation.

Laura: But your appropriation will be slow in coming, won't it?

Sellers: Oh, bless you, no. What! with the Senator, and, Mulberry Sellers, and Lafayette Hawkins, all working for it, you'll see Congress surrender fast enough. But do you think I'm sitting around idle meantime? No, indeed. I've got some enormous operations on foot. But I'm keeping quiet. Your old hand don't go pow-wow-ing around and letting everybody find out his little game. Now there's a speculation in corn, that looks well. Some New York parties want me to put some capital in with them—buy up the growing crops of thirteen states, and boss the market, when the grain matures. There's oceans of money in it, and it don't take much capital— two millions will do it, or two millions and a half at the outside. I haven't promised yet, but the thing looks well.

Laura: What can you want better than that?

Sellers: [With mystery] Ah, well, corn is good, but there's better things still—There's a little operation in hogs, that I'm considering. Buy up all the hogs in the country, at an easy figure, & then just shut down on the slaughter houses, till they come to our terms. See! The price would tower, tower, why a hog would become jewelry— Talk about style, keeping carriages, & all that sort of thing. Why you'd hear a man say "there goes old Smith—rich?—well, he keeps his hog!" I've calculated all the chances & there's millions in it.

Mrs Hawkins: [Aside] Hear the man talk—I *never*. Such an eternal old mill to grind out fortunes!

Sellers: And hogs, ain't everything—not by any manner of means. I've got a little patent medicine invention on hand that'll revolutionize the universe—I only lack one ingredient.

Mrs Hawkins: [Aside] Oh, yes, he only lacks one ingredient. That's what was the matter with his plagued perpetual motion machine that wouldn't go.

Sellers: When I find out what that ingredient is you'll hear of Mulberry Sellers' Infallible, Imperial, Oriental, Optic Liniment, and Salvation for sore eyes! The medical wonder of the age. I can make it for 30 cents a barrel—and sell it for halfa—dollar a bottle—Just reflect on the prospect—Sell 50,000 bottles the first year—clear profit $24,000. 200,000 the second year, clear profit $96,000—third year sell a million bottles, clear profit, four hundred & ninety odd thousand dollars. Then waltz over to Europe. Next year Asia—and I tell you, there's your eye—water market! Population, sixteen hundred millions of human beings, and every last one of them *born* with sore eyes. In less than one year our income from Asia alone would be goodness knows *how* many millions and millions, & billions of money!—

[Enter Hawkins]

Hawkins: Well, Nancy, the man's gone.

Mrs Hawkins: And—and—you didn't sell the land, Si?

Hawkins: Oh, Nancy I—I *couldn't*. I hadn't the heart to rob the children. He only offered five thousand.

Mrs Hawkins: Oh, Si, Si—I won't complain, but its hard, it's very hard. [Covers her face]

Hawkins: Oh, *don't* grieve so—I can't bear it. I am a fool and heartless—There, there, I'll run after him—he shall have it at his own price—*half* his own price—[Starting to go, Sellers seizes him].

Sellers: Si. Hawkins, do you mean to say you're going to sell the Tennessee land?

Hawkins: Indeed I do.

Sellers: Preposterous! Stay right where you are! [Nearly overcome but recovers] Thank heaven I've got here in time to save you!

Hawkins: How? What do you mean?

Sellers: Why man, we are going to get three millions for that land! It's as good as done.

Hawkins: Tell me all about it, Sellers, tell me quick. How near I came to making an ass of myself.

Sellers: Hawkins you're a friend of mine, I'll let you into a secret.

Hawkins: A Secret?

Laura: May I know what it is?

Sellers: Come here! Gather around close—walls have ears—[all gather around Sellers]. Senator Dilworthy and I have talked it all over.

Hawkins: Talked it over?

Sellers: The land.

Hawkins: Well? Well?

Sellers: We have our plans.

Hawkins: Well, Well, your plans—

Sellers: The Senator is a philanthropist. He is the father of the poor down—trodden negro—

Hawkins: Indeed? I had no idea—

Sellers: Metaphorically speaking—Metaphorically speaking. He is their Moses, their Aaron—their benefactor.

Hawkins: But the land! The land!

Sellers: I'm coming to the land. This glorious union has set the Negro free. What is the next step?

Hawkins: Support him, I suppose.

Sellers: Well—a—not exactly, not exactly. Prepare him to support himself. Educate him—Make him a skilled workman. How shall we do this? Establish a university where instruction shall be given in all industries. Where shall that university be located? In the knobs of East Tennessee. Why there? Because there all minerals abound, coal, iron, copper—splendid forests, fields, pastures!—*Everything* that's wanted. How shall the nation become possessed of this noble domain? Let Congress buy it!

Hawkins: Heavens, what an idea!

Sellers: [Tapping his forehead] Mine. The Senator grasped it at once. It was he—an impartial umpire—who named the figure— three millions.

Hawkins: [Aglow] It's worth it. It'll be worth it, and more. And is the Senator willing to take charge of the bill?

Sellers: Willing? His love for the Negro alone actuates him—in the matter. There will be opposition. Men without heart, destitute of philanthropy will see a job in it. Let them. We defy calumny.

Laura: But is there a chance of success?

Sellers: Why the thing is sure. Senator Dilworthy said to me, "Col. Sellers, with your aid on the outside & the help of Providence on the inside, the thing can be carried through." Now the Senator is not a fast man, he goes slow, but he goes sure. He carries too much solid religion to be a—frisky—as you may say—He'll bring the whole religious influence of the country to the support of this gigantic scheme for the amelioration of the Negro.

Hawkins: [Excitedly] Day is breaking at last—Ah, Nancy, do you wish I had taken the paltry five thousand?

Mrs Hawkins: Si—Whatever you do is right & contents me-but I'm afraid—[Enter Clay plainly but well dressed. Mr & Mrs Hawkins rush to meet him.] Oh, Clay is come!

Hawkins: Why, Clay! Clay! [All shake hands. Clay kisses Mrs Hawkins, & advances to Laura, who holds back shyly.]

Clay: Laura, have you no welcome for me?

Laura: [Giving her cheek to kiss] Yes a thousand welcomes, for [in a low voice] though I know I have torn your faithful heart, there is that in your eyes which tells me you do not hate me.

Clay: [In a low tone] My Darling—Sister—you will never see *that* day!

Laura: [In a low voice] Oh, I am so grateful.

Clay: [Turning to the others] Mother, I read your letter, and I respond in the words of the old song, Mother dear. "I give thee all, I can no more though poor the offering be." [Hands Mrs Hawkins a package]

Mrs Hawkins: [Opening package, discovers bank bills] O, Clay. [Kisses him] You good soul. [Kiss] Two Hundred Dollars. [Kiss] It saves the whole household from suffering. [Several kisses]

Clay: One can't scrape much together plodding along at low wages, Mother dear, but next year I'll have more.

Sellers: [Advancing] Let's shake hands again, Clay—you're a splendid fellow—splendid fellow. But you shouldn't waste your time this way.

Clay: Waste my time?

Sellers: How long did it take you to earn that money?

Clay: Well—nearly a year.

Sellers: There! Now think of that! Sheer waste of time. Why when we get the Columbia River appropriation, town lots in Napoleon will be worth a thousand dollars a front foot, and there'll be ten thousand of them. How does that strike you for our speculation?

Clay: Where is Columbia River?

Sellers: It used to be called Goose Run.

Clay: And Napoleon?

Sellers: Stone Landing.

Clay: And the appropriation?

Sellers: Congress will pass it next year.

Clay: Very well, sail along in the clouds, old friend, nature gave you the necessary wings, but she only made a plodder of me, & so I think I'll stick to it.

Hawkins: [Approaching & shaking hands with Clay] You are right, Clay—You are really the only wise one among us. Nancy, you can pay Johnson, now, and perhaps you can find Clay something to eat.

Mrs Hawkins: That I will. [Exit]

Sellers: Clay, perhaps you're right—you're a square good fellow any way—and when the town lots come into market, you shan't be forgotten—meantime—for a few days only—[Whispers] [Clay offers 20 or 30 dollars]—thank you—no, only a ten. [Taking it] Couldn't take more than a ten on any account. I'll make a note of it. Never forget these little financial transactions.

Clay: Don't mention it, Colonel.

Sellers: [Reflecting] Well, I won't. [Exit]

Clay: [Approaches Laura who is standing] Laura!

Laura: Well, Clay—

Clay: Are you vexed with me, Laura?

Laura: I was when you first wrote.

Clay: And now?

Laura: Now I know you wrote so, from love of me.

Clay: Oh, how dearly I *have* loved you, all these long, long years, and always shall. But it is hopeless, and has been, ever since that unhappy day that—but I will not speak of that, for it can only distress us both. But now I am come to you only as a loving brother, whose sister's happiness holds the first place in his heart. [Advances & takes her hand, her head inclines & she is agitated.] I will be ever so gentle, but we must talk of this matter. Laura, dear, look at me. Never before have your eyes shrunk from mine. [Pause] Still silent?

Laura: [Her head still bowed] Oh, Clay it is hard. What do you ask of me?

Clay: Only what I asked in my letter. Who is Col. Selby?

Laura: He was an officer in the confederate service.

Clay: But what is he to you?

Laura: A Friend.

Clay: No more?

Laura: Oh, Clay, why do you ask these questions?

Clay: I will tell you, Laura, these questions have been asked of me.

Laura: [Looking up] Fools! Why do people trouble themselves about me?

Clay: Because you live in the world & are a part of it. Now will you answer, not "people" but me?

Laura: Spare me! trust me!

Clay: I would spare you if I could. I have trusted you. [Pauses] You have not answered.

Laura: I cannot.

Clay: Then I shall ask the only other person in the world who can answer.

Laura: Clay! Clay! there is a limit beyond which even you must not go!

Clay: That limit I have not yet reached.

Laura: Clay.

Clay: Laura, you & I were thrown by a strange chance into the bosom of an honest & generous family. There may be wiser men than he whom we call father, but there are none kinder, none truer, none more devoted. We bear his name, by his good courtesy, and it behooves us to bear it worthily.

Laura: Clay, you forget! You insult me!

Clay: I insult you! Oh Laura, if you could look into my heart! If you could know how carefully I would guard your name from the lightest breath of suspicion, you would see how capable I am of any crime but that—

Laura: You saved my life, nine years ago, at the peril of your own. Would you kill me now? Clay, Clay, you are killing me!

Clay: If I am killing you, Laura, it is because it is time for you to die—

Laura: [Sinking on her knees] Oh, what do your words mean? [Clay exhibits strong emotion, but after a moment controls it, he approaches Laura, bends over her, & caresses her head.]

Clay: Poor Child! Poor Child! you love him?

Laura: I—love him.

Clay: [After a pause] And you know now—do you not? You know now—

Laura: [Raising her head] Know what?

Clay: That he is a—villain!

Laura: [Springing to her feet] Clay, you shall not speak so of him! It was all my fault.

Clay: Your fault, Laura? You—proud, chaste, cold to men who wooed you honorably. Your fault! I'll not believe it! You seek to screen him from the punishment he deserves.

Laura: What do you mean? No one has wooed me otherwise than honorably.

Clay: No one? Has Col. Selby asked you to become his wife?

Laura: He has.

Clay: And you—speak truly—speak without fear—you?

Laura: I am—his—wife—

Clay: Oh, this is frightful! Ah my poor Laura! My darling sister! Does God permit such things to be?

Laura: Clay, is it so terrible? I love him, he loves me.

Clay: Loves you! Coward! Reptile!—Laura, die, if you can! Col. Selby has a Wife in New Orleans—!

[Laura falls senseless. Clay kneels beside her.]

Curtain falls

Act 3d *Scene 1st A lapse of two months, A shabbily furnished room in Col. Sellers' house—Enter Sellers & Clay Hawkins.*

Sellers: You find things looking a little careless, here Clay—but I just set about refurnishing and frescoing. Yes, Yes, it's as you were *saying* Clay! Hawkins, ain't the man he used to be: don't grasp an idea as he did once. But your Brother Lafayette's a rising young man, and will make his mark. Senator Dilworthy writes that he has great influence in Washington. Knows all the members. Knows their wives, knows their babies, knows all the society ladies. Lafayette, will pull the appropriation through without buying a vote—that's more than every young man can do in these days. He can count himself worth a million, the day that that bill becomes a law.

Clay: But Colonel, the whole appropriation is only $200,000.

Sellers: True—but it breeds the railroads—the railroad breeds population—up go your town lots into the thousands, and there you are! See?

Clay: What railroad?

Sellers: [Confidentially] The Salt Lake Pacific extension is going to run through Napoleon.

Clay: Indeed? I don't see why it *should*. Napoleon's full twenty miles out of the straight line of the road.

Sellers: No man can know what a straight line is until the Engineers have gone over it. I have talked with Jeff Thompson, the division engineer. Jeff understands the wants of Napoleon. Jeff says railroads ought to be run for the benefit of the Company & the general country round—not for the benefit of towns already built. Now how is the Company to make money out of a railroad? Is it by going to the old towns, where the land is all owned by Tom, Dick & Harry? *No* Sir! It's by going to new places, where the land is owned by the Company.

Clay: Ah, I understand.

Sellers: We—the Company & myself—have secured 15 miles square in the heart of Napoleon—or, at present Napoleon's in the heart of *it*. The Company will hold one half, myself & friends the other half. The appropriation will widen & straighten Columbia River, & thus we connect Steamer & Railroad. It's a grand scheme, Clay— a noble scheme. What should you say to a City built up like the rod of Aladdin had touched it, and you could own the land?

Clay: It looks great—on paper.

Sellers: It is the grandest enterprise of the age!—a million spent on Columbia River, will make Napoleon, worth five millions.

Clay: And the Government finds the million, while the Rail Road Company owns the town?

Sellers: Exactly, my dear boy, exactly. That's what Governments are for. It's only within the last few years, that the science of government has been thoroughly understood. Our fore fathers never had statesmen like ours.

Clay: I *believe* you. [Rising] Well, Col., success to you. Speculation is not in my line.

Sellers: Not in your line? Clay, you are one of us; Laura is one of us. Why, Clay, I wouldn't take ten millions if I couldn't share it with my friends.

Clay: I know that as well as I know anything old friend. You always give your money away as fast as you get it, and so for the sake of the unfortunate I want to see you swim in wealth yet. But I must go.

Sellers: Go! What has Mulberry Sellers done that you should walk out of his house, upon the very stroke of the dinner hour! Polly, Polly, hurry up your dinner, dear!

Clay: [Aside] The simple—hearted old soul, I mustn't let him uncover his poverty. [Aloud] Thank—you Col. you must excuse me—some other day—

Sellers: No, my boy, my boy. I make this a personal matter. [Calls] Fly around, Polly, Clay's going to dine with us. [Enter Mrs Sellers, who throws up her hands in a helpless way, then motions Sellers to approach.] That's right, Clay, draw up to the stove, and warm yourself. [Clay draws up to a rickety stove, lighted within with a candle—stove door, propped to, with the poker leaned against it— Sellers approaches Mrs Sellers.]

Mrs Sellers: Oh, Mulberry, how could you? There's nothing in the house to eat.

Sellers: [Staggered]—Nothing, Polly. Nothing?

Mrs Sellers: Nothing in the world but raw turnips, & cold water.

Sellers: [Disconcerted] By George! Why *didn't* I speak to you before I—run! Can't very well back down from the invitation now. [Recovering his customary confidence] O never mind, raw turnips & water will do—if it's a good article of water. But provide the best, provide the best the market affords, Polly. It's a close place, but cheer up, girl, cheer up. Providence, will tide us over the scrape somehow. Don't let us ever weaken on Providence, sweetheart. [Clay trips foot in poker, & exposes candle. Sellers nonplussed. Awkward pause on both sides. Then Sellers recovers.] Little idea of mine, one of the greatest things in the world. I have been reading European, Scientific reports. I saw in a moment, that heat was a non—conductor, & of course it's influence must be deadly in a nervous organization where there is any tendency to Rheumatism.

What you want is the appearance of heat, so no one can have rheumatism in my house. Don't forget to write to your father, tell him it's my own idea. [Placing chairs at table] Come, Clay, we always dine simply, on Thursdays, but it's a healthy diet. [Clay glances at table & takes seat. Mrs S. sits opposite Sellers, who rolls back his sleeves airily, & proceeds to place the turnips daintily on plates, & pass them.] Let me tell you, Clay, things are looking pretty bright now—the air is full of money. I wouldn't take three fortunes for one little operation I've got on hand. Anything from the casters? No? You're right—perfectly right. Some people prefer mustard with turnips, but I take them plain. None of your embellishments for Mulberry Sellers! High living kills our best men. Take some more water—there's plenty of it—help yourself. How does the fruit strike you.

Clay: [Aside] Well, this is—this is-if there's one thing that I hate with my whole heart, it is a raw turnip—and the water will make them swell, and—[aloud] Oh, excellent, Colonel excellent!

Sellers: I thought you'd like them. Examine them; examine them—they'll bear it. See how hard & tough they are. They can't start any turnips like these in *this* part of the country. These came from New Jersey—imported them myself. They cost like sin—but Lord bless you, I go in for having the best of everything, if it does cost a little. Poor economy to save on your nourishment. These are the early Malcolm. It's a turnip that can't be produced, except in just one orchard, and the supply never *is* up to the demand. I'll try and get a few barrels for you. [Clay declines by action] The plague can't come where these turnips are.

Clay: The plague? What plague?

Sellers: Why, the old regular Asiatic plague that nearly depopulated London some two centuries ago.

Clay: But how does that concern *us*—there's no plague here.

Sellers: [Impressively] Sh—h—! I've let it out! Well never mind, keep it to yourself. You know Dr. McDowell, the great Surgeon? Well, he let me into a little secret about the plague. It's a coming booming along. In three months it'll be waltzing through the land like a whirlwind, anyone it lays its hand on has got to make out his will. The only thing to prevent it, is raw turnips & cold water. You just eat from six to eight raw turnips at every meal & drink from a pint & a half to two quarts of water, you may defy the plague.

Clay: [Aside] And bring on Cholera—I begin to feel it in my vitals now—[Aloud] I am glad you told me Colonel. [In evident discomfort] I—I am—very grateful.

Sellers: Don't *mention* it my boy! You're like one of the family. I could have kept it from you but I wouldn't—*You* know Mulberry Sellers—But don't reveal the remedy, to even your particular friends.

Clay: [Aside] No, but I will to my enemies.

Sellers: McDowell would just kill me. Take some more water—you can't drink too much water with turnips, the water absorbs the turnip, give your appetite full swing, you'll feel like a fighting cock tomorrow.

Clay: [Aside despondently] I feel as if I had swallowed an unappeasable wildcat—[Messenger enters with letter—Sellers glances at superscription—and rises with a flourish].

Sellers: Polly; that's from Dilworthy, that's his Christian hand. I'll wager you a corner lot in the heart of Napoleon that the appropriation's past—

Mrs Sellers: Open it Berry!—open it.

Sellers: Will you excuse me Clay?

Clay: Certainly Colonel.

Sellers: [Opens letter] Rejoice with me my friend. Providence has crowned our efforts with success. [With emotion] Did you ever hear anything more touching? What a character! Splendid man is Dilworthy! Would that our Country had more Statesmen like Dilworthy—

Clay: [Rising] Allow me to congratulate you—

Sellers: Thank you my boy, thank you.

Clay: [Standing & just perceptibly betraying pain—using his hands uneasily & unconsciously putting one above his stomach.] [Aside] I am so disordered. I never had such a heart burn in my life. [Exit Clay]

Sellers: Come Polly, let's go & spread the welcome news, we are rich now, you shall have a bran new silk gown to—morrow. Give those turnips to the poor. Providence will take care of the plague. [Throws letter on table. Exit Mr & Mrs Sellers.] [Laura enters]

Laura: I thought I should find Clay, here. Where can he have gone? [Sees letter] What is this? A letter? [Does not open it, but looks at the frank] This is Senator Dilworthy's frank—so it is from him. Thank heaven I can see a way out of this place at last. Everyone looks upon me with suspicion. Clay pities me. Pities *me!* What have I done? I married a villain, married him secretly, persuaded of a necessity by his lies, and blinded by my boundless trust in him. I made him my idol, & he has trampled me in the dust. The world smiles on him & looks questioningly on me. If it knew all, it would cast me out to die in the streets, with its fine sense of justice—But my secret is safe in Clay's hands. No license is required in Missouri in order to marry—so there is no record of that kind to betray me. Justices of the peace keep no records—and the justice who married us is dead. The world is open to me so long as I continue to deceive it—There must be a place for a woman like me—a woman with beauty in her face, and a demon in her heart. For two months he has not come near me. He abandons me, but I'll not forget him. [Enter Col. Selby—she starts, but recovers her unconcern. He advances—She glances towards him.] Ah, Col. Selby, is it you! I did not recognize you at first.

Col. Selby: Am I so greatly changed, Laura?

Laura: [Looking at him with more attention] You are changed I think—You are older—There is more silver in your hair, than when I last saw you.

Col. Selby: When you last saw me? Scarcely two months ago!

Laura: Is it two months? I did not think it was so long.

Col. Selby: [Aside] What the deuce is the matter with the Girl— this is a new & interesting phase in her character. [To Laura] I heard that you had been ill?

Laura: I *have* been ill.

Col. Selby: Nothing serious I hope?

Laura: Nothing serious—a slight affection of the heart—I am fully recovered.

Col. Selby: Were you concerned, at my absence?

Laura: I? Why should I be?

Col. Selby: I had a reason for not coming to say good-bye.

Laura: Had you? Ah, I remember now. You disappeared the same day my brother Clay came home. I remember, people spoke of it.

Col. Selby: What did people say?

Laura: That your disappearance was timed with very clever judgement, very intelligent discretion.

Col. Selby: That is to say, they intimated that I ran away from your Brother?

Laura: They intimated it, but it is absurd—a soldier, an officer— certainly would not run away from a young man who has never been in military life at all.

Col. Selby: I did run away from him.

Laura: Indeed?

Col. Selby: If I had remained, we should have fought.

Laura: Well—Since when have military gentlemen been so averse from fighting?

Col. Selby: Since Military gentlemen have been in nature like other Gentlemen. Clay is your Brother.

Laura: Well—he is, I believe a Gentleman.

Col. Selby: A Gentleman, undoubtedly; but if we had fought, people would have asked why.

Laura: True.

Col. Selby: And if their questions produced no information, they would have indulged in surmises.

Laura: I am to understand then, that in running away, you performed a very magnanimous act.

Col. Selby: It was an act that saved your honor, at some sacrifice to my own.

Laura: You were very considerate. I ought to feel grateful. I would perhaps if—

Col. Selby: If what?

Laura: If you had not returned.

Col. Selby: [After a pause] Laura, you were here.

Laura: [Flings upon him a glance of scorn, then resumes her bantering tone.] How well you act! You must have rehearsed frequently.

Col. Selby: [Resuming his reserve of manner] As you will—I have no right to approach you.

Laura: [Gazes at him a moment, pauses, then walks away, restrains passion, but presently it breaks forth] Oh, I *cannot* help it. I love him. I love him, and I thought I *hated* him, as God knows I *ought*. Will nothing break these fetters! [Buries her face. Selby approaches.]

Col. Selby: Laura, I have wronged you shamefully—I was a miscreant. If my life will atone for my sin, take it. Losing you, I lose all that makes my life worth the living.

Laura: [Her face still buried] Oh, George, George, if you ever loved me, how could you deceive me so cruelly.

Col. Selby: How could I? Did not the deception give me you?

Laura: [Rising suddenly] And how have you left me? You found me young, ignorant, trusting. Now only six months later—I am old in heart, wise in experience, without faith in God, or the honor of man.

Col. Selby: Laura, these reproaches are as useless as they are distressing. I confess my crime. Now, I plead with you to listen to reason. You can be a child no longer—be a woman—a woman of the world.

Laura: A Woman of the world?

Col. Selby: Listen. I have been loveless all my life. In the gushing weakness of youth, I listened to the beseechings of my father, and saved him from bankruptcy by marrying a girl who was poor in spirit, poor in mind, poor in affection, poor in health, poor in everything but money. My punishment, has been heavy—and hers no less—for our detestation is mutual. I found you, a beautiful young girl, and I was tranced, chained, helpless. I could not resist— I could not go away. O, think how the age long famine in my heart must have welcomed the rich abundance of your love! Laura, if I had been single—you *know*—your own heart *tells* you—I would have married you! But being married, I-I-deceived you. You thought you were my wife—while in truth you were not. Was the fault yours? Were you less pure because I was vile?

Laura: Oh, why recall the dreadful memories!

Col. Selby: Simply to show you, that you have not forfeited honor. You are sinless. I am the sinner. Society would condemn you if it knew, but society need not know.

Laura: Alas, our world is so small.

Col. Selby: There is a larger world than this you move in. Senator Dilworthy is my friend. You will be invited to Washington—we shall meet there—shall it be as friends?

Laura: As friends?

Col. Selby: Laura, I have said that if I had been unmarried when we met, I would have married you. [With a meaning look] To those who can wait—there is hope!

Laura: Then you love me! You do love me!

Col. Selby: Love you darling! [He opens his arms]

Laura: [Is about to spring into his arms, but checks herself, waves him beseechingly away.] O, it is wrong! It is wrong! Do not tempt me!

Clay: [Who has entered from rear, advances. Draws pistol.] [To Selby] Are you armed?

Col. Selby: I am.

Clay: Defend yourself. [Laura seizes his arm]

Col. Selby: Not against you.

Col. Sellers: [Entering] Stop!

Clay: What Colonel: Are you his shield?

Sellers: Not his, but yours, Clay. You cannot kill a man who won't defend himself.

Tableau and curtain

Act 4th Scene 1st Washington
[Room in Dilworthy's house, richly furnished. Emily and Lafayette Hawkins discovered elegantly dressed.]

Emily: Did you ever see anything like the way Laura's been sweeping things here in Washington!

Lafayette: Never anything like it! Why she's got half the town at her feet!

Emily: My! & don't she sift her blandishments around! She just marches on any old iceberg of a Congressman & melts him right down with a smile or two.

Lafayette: I don't believe there's another woman in the world that can do it. She'll lobby that land bill of ours straight through both houses of Congress *easy!*

Emily: And then we'll be rich! & won't I have a new dress three times a week!

Lafayette: O say *six* times a week!

Emily: Well I *will*. And I'll marry an *Admiral* or a General, *too*.

Lafayette: Well, how people do change their notions about things— *You* for instance.

Emily: Me! Look at Laura! She used to want to be a soldier, or a nurse in a military hospital. And now this wild fashionable life here has blown all that sort of ambition to the winds. And yet I don't believe she's happy, for all her splendid notoriety & being glorified & worshiped by everybody.

Lafayette: Well are you happy?

Emily: No, I *ain't*. And that's a fact. But O me, I *was*, when I was a simple, simpering idiot in Missouri. [Enter Laura]

Lafayette: Laura, dear, we've been talking about you—& how in six months you have become the belle of Washington.

Laura: Ah, you were always too enthusiastic about me my dear brother—

Lafayette: It is not I, Sister, & it isn't *us*—it is everybody. You have in your train a dozen Senators, a score or so of Congressmen, two or three Cabinet Officers, and—

Laura: That will do Lafayette—There is but one President. If the Tennessee land bill passes—

Lafayette: He will sign it! You carry the magicians wand, Laura. Everybody yields to you.

Laura: [Rising & walking] [Passionately] I live on excitement. For five days I have not slept, and am not fatigued.

Lafayette: But you *must* rest, Laura—you'll be ill—

Laura: Rest! Ah, yes, if I only could!

Lafayette: Well, good luck *is* disturbing. It will be three millions, if the land bill passes—& it's sure to pass. And we came near selling once for five thousand dollars.

Laura: But we did not sell. Come, Lafayette, we must go to the House of Representatives—the fight has begun—Come Emily. I'll drop you at Senator Thompson's if you are going that way, come. [Exit Laura & Emily]

Lafayette: What is the matter with that Girl? She's as hard & brilliant as a diamond these last two or three days. I don't like that Col. Selby, he's too attentive altogether. I must speak to her. [Exit] [Enter Uncle Daniel followed by Colonel Sellers, bottle in hand, and just a mere trifle tight.]

Sellers: Hic! I've found the lacking ingredient! The eye—water's a success—I tried it on one eye & I couldn't see for four or five hours—shows how strong it is. [Sits in chair] Daniel!

Uncle Dan'l: Yes, sah.

Sellers: Where's your Mars Lafayette?

Uncle Dan'l: He's just done gone up stahs, sah, b—but he be down directly, sah.

Sellers: Uncle Dan'l, [hic] you stammer bad as ever don't you?

Uncle Dan'l: Jes the same M—Mars Sellers—can't git rid o'dat.

Sellers: [Hic] Why don't you try the eye—water? That'll cure anything, take it internally, externally or [hic] eternally.

Uncle Dan'l: No, Mars Sellers, a-a-ain't no use, Sah—tain't no use. I done tried lots o'truck.

Sellers: Dan'l you've got no faith. Stammering is easily cured. I knew a man once that was cured a perfect [hic] cure. He told me all about it. I was sitting all alone by myself in the tavern at Hawkeye, when a man came in & looked at me from head to foot & then he walked away, presently he sidled up again & touched me on the shoulder and says. I th-th-th-(Whew!) think I've seen you before. Well, I says, perhaps you have but what makes you whistle so? Says he! I'll te-te-(Whew!) tell you. You see I used to st-st-(Whew!) st-(Whew!) stammer, so you couldn't make out anything I had to say!—I was co-co-(Whew!) courting a girl & she said she didn't want to marry a man with such a hor—such a hor-(Whew!)ible an infirmity. So I went to a doctor, & he told me every time I wanted to st-st-(Whew!) stammer I must wh-wh-(Whew!) whistle so I did & it cu-cu-(Whew!) cured me. [Exit Dan'l, Laughing & Whistling] [Enter Lafayette]

Lafayette: Col. Sellers! Something wrong with the Columbia River enterprise old friend, or *you* wouldn't wander so far from Hawkeye!

Sellers: [Holding Lafayette's hand and beaming] Ah, Lafayette, I've foun' (Hic!)—I've foun' (Hic!). [Breaks into benevolent smile] How's Laura?

Lafayette: Laura is well. Pretty busy, but in good spirits. How are things at Napoleon?

Sellers: Napoleon's there, the river's there, but the boys wanted to hang me!

Lafayette: *Hang* you!—Why my dear Col. what have you done?

Sellers: Nothing, that's what they wanted to hang me for. They wanted to hang me because I couldn't pay them. I couldn't pay them because the President of the Company wouldn't honor my draft. Now if they had wanted to hang him it would have met with my entire approbation, but when they made it a personal matter I took a change of venue.

Lafayette: You ran away?

Sellers: [Emphatically] *No* sir. I rode away. There was two hundred very rough looking men there & I don't want to hurt anyone, my horse was near by & it wasn't far to the depot, & I'm—here—

Lafayette: Good—you've come just in time. I'm to have an interview with the President of the Company this afternoon & will make him disgorge.

Sellers: My dear boy, it won't do. I have had an interview with him, and he *won't* disgorge. He says that in spite of all our work, we owe him ten thousand dollars!

Lafayette: Ten thousand dollars! *Impossible.*

Sellers: Well, he's got it down in black & white & says the appropriation was eaten up in getting the bill through Congress & that we owe for our assessments—

Lafayette: There is some villainy here—

Sellers: I know, but we're too good to find it out, we're too honest for this part of the country. Let us go west—Young man. (Hic!) Go west.

Lafayette: Go West! Did it ever occur to you, Colonel, that you were by no means, the sort of a man to be hiding your capacities in the obscurities of the West? *You ought to be in Congress*—

Sellers: [After a pause—gravely] Lafayette, I have known you ever since you were a child. I've seen you grow to manhood. I've known your Father, but what have I ever done to you to justify you in making a remark *like that.*

Lafayette: My Dear Colonel, I did not mean to offend you—

Sellers: It's all right my boy! It's all right! But I've got a little pride left in my character yet & it goes right to my heart to hear you say a thing like that. [Enter Laura]

Laura: [Excitedly] I've just heard that the bill has passed the House of Representatives, clear two thirds vote! The three millions are almost ours! Ah Colonel Sellers! is that you? [Shakes hands with Col.]

Sellers: Why how do you do. I congratulate you, I congratulate you with all my (Hic!) heart. Three million's plenty—plenty to start in with & make a fortune. But it never pours but it rains—I've found the lacking ingredient.

Laura: I see you have old friend—But what are you dreaming about Lafayette?

Lafayette: Well, I was just thinking—

Laura: But this is no time to be thinking. Be off to Newspaper Row & see if you can't give the correspondents an item or two about the land bill.

Sellers: Excuse me (Hic!) I want to go with you. I want to know the Newspaper boys. I like them, they're so talented & so full of piousness, they're chuck full of piousness—ness all the time.

Lafayette: [Aside] Well, I never saw the old man so before, his eye—water, is a trifle too powerful.

Sellers: I'll see you later, Miss Laura—

Laura: The door's always open to you Colonel. [Exit Sellers & Lafayette arm in arm. She walks up & down stage.] At last!—at last, the prize I have toiled for—without humiliation, in so many ways that would have made me blush, in the old days before my heart was hardened, & my soul seared, is almost mine! And now, after all that it has cost, I care nothing for it—nothing, nothing—it so shrinks into insignificance in presence of a matter of mightier consequence. To—morrow—how far away it seems—how Washington will ring. Am I in my senses? Is this indeed I?—O, the dread mystery of a woman's heart! Oh, will none save me from myself! Clay, Clay, why have you delayed? You would have given me strength! I would have put this temptation away. I am going down—down—down—out of the world, I have held at my feet. O, George, George, if I had never seen you! [Enter Col. Selby] [She is about to throw herself into his arms—he by a gesture restrains her.]

Col. Selby: I have called, Laura, in obedience to your commands.

Laura: In obedience to my commands? Was it not understood—

Col. Selby: Let us understand each other at last. I hoped to avoid this explanation, but circumstances have forced me to it.

Laura: George—I—I—do not comprehend.

Col. Selby: You have had time to reflect. It is not *possible* that you are still wild enough, foolish enough to abandon friends, to throw away name, fame, *everything* and fly with me to Europe!

Laura: To the *world's end* George, if the World has an end!

Col. Selby: I appreciate your devotion, but I have reflected, though *you* have not; and I cannot accept the sacrifice; I love you too well—

Laura: *You—love* me! You mock me! You cast me off!

Col. Selby: Laura, when you came here six months ago, you were an obscure girl, seemingly you had no future. The world took little note of what you did, whom you loved, or who loved you— *Now*, all that is changed. You are one of the best know women in Washington. Events of the day give absolute assurance that you will shortly come into possession of great riches—Your parents live— your brothers live—and above all my Wife lives.

Laura: And you remind me of this?—You—

Col. Selby: Be calm, Laura—reflect—

Laura: Reflect! I was simple, innocent & trusting. Day by day, patiently, perseveringly, with infernal art, you wound your toils about me—day by day, hour by hour, until my heart, my soul, myself was yours. Knowing all the consequences, the awful awakening that must come to me in time, you yet could find it in your nature to do this heartless thing—I thought myself your Wife—and was only your silly dupe—once you abandoned me and I tried to forget & live. Then you came again, and whispered in my ears the words that are to a betrayed woman, as are promises of liberty to hopeless captives that have grown old in dungeons. You said the day was coming—and coming soon—when I should hold in honor, & in undisputed right, the name & place of Wife to you. And now, you tell me that your Wife still lives! & so the lying hope you raised from the dead must betake itself to the grave and the worms again.

Col. Selby: Your memory is singularly faithful. What do you propose to do about it?

Laura: Do? Humble myself in the dust at your feet—appeal to the remnant of that manhood that once made you great and good, and generous, plead with you as a lost soul pleads for pity. Oh, I walk in the valley of the shadow of death, put forth your hand & save me. [Kneels]

Selby: Come now this is fine—Really you ought to be on the stage.

Laura: Don't mock me George—be merciful!

Selby: Oh, stay on your knees if you like it—but I may as well close this farce—it has ceased to amuse. My poor country bred girl, you were a trifle too confiding—pshaw—marry *you*—that is *too* good. I am a gentleman born. I marry you—a vulgar upstart—an empty doll of shoddy fashion.

Laura: George Selby—Do you dare talk to me like this?

Selby: Dare? Why what can you do?

Laura: The Law shall teach you what I can do.

Selby: The Law! Well this is innocence—that most noble sham the Law!

Laura: The law can protect me & it shall—

Selby: Of course it will, ha! ha! It has been tried so often. It always sends the man away with a pious warning against future designing women—and tells the *woman* if she sins again she'd better beware. Oh, go to law by all means. Fool! why if my Wife were dead & buried in the bottom of the sea I would not mate with your sort.

Laura: Oh, this is infamous. Infamous!

Selby: You were a trifle too confiding.

Laura: To the winds, with the Law. I was a woman weak & humble, but I am a *devil* now. You lied to me—betrayed me—jeered at me—and yet you venture here! Fool, idiot—to bear your head to the lightnings of a wrath.

Selby: Peace child—you are—

Laura: Mad and you have made me so. Do you know what it is to drive a woman like me to madness? It is death. [Shoots him] [She kneels over the body, caresses it—looks up with a vacant stare.] I have killed the only man I ever loved. [Enter Col. Sellers, Lafayette & others]

All: Laura, Laura, what is this?

Laura: It is death!

Tableau & Curtain

Act 5th The Court Room Judge on bench—Jury in box—Counsel etc.

Sheriff: O, Yes. O, Yes. O, Yes, the first district court of Columbia is duly opened!—

Judge: Are the counsel ready to proceed with the trial of Laura Hawkins.

Counsel: Ready your honor.

Judge: Let the prisoner be brought in—[Exit Sheriff—all present lean forward to see the prisoner—Enter Laura, leaning on Sellers arm—she is richly & tastefully dressed in black. Following her are sheriff—Mr & Mrs Hawkins—Clay, Lafayette etc. Laura is led to seat.]

D. Attorney: [Who is one of the snarling, sneering brow-beating class of lawyers. He is bitter & loud.] John Peterson will take the stand! [Peterson enters witness box] Mr. Peterson, in your examination on behalf of the prisoner, yesterday, you testified that you had been a servant in the Dilworthy mansion for about a year. Is this true sir? Come, speak up!

Peterson: Yes, sir.

D. Attorney: And you had formed the opinion that the prisoner at the bar was insane. Is this also true sir? Eh?

Peterson: Yes, sir.

D. Attorney: Have they paid you anything for this? Have you *charged* anything for this valuable assistance?

Peterson: Charged anything?

D. Attorney: Charged anything? Don't repeat my question—but answer it.

Peterson: No, sir. I haven't charged anything—it was my honest impression.

D. Attorney: [Sneeringly] You've a very honest countenance John—in the dark. Now Mr. Peterson throughout this whole affair you've shown a curious anxiety—a *very* curious anxiety to befriend the prisoner at the bar. Is she anything to you?

Peterson: She stood by my old Mother when she was poor and in distress & hadn't a friend in the world.

D. Attorney: Ah, very kind of her & very romantic. So you thought one good turn deserves another & you've come here to shield the prisoner at the bar, with your weighty opinion that she's insane. Now, sir, what do you know about insanity—Eh?

Peterson: I only thought she acted like it—

D. Attorney: Acted! You needn't say another word. Acting describes it admirably. In these days every murderer knows the expediency of acting a little—the insanity dodge is the only sure card now-a-days.

Peterson: Miss Hawkins always befriended me.

D. Attorney: Silence, Sir. Wait till you're spoken too, wait till you're asked, then give us the tender relations existing between you & the prisoner, put them in a Sunday School story book, to soft—soap the heathen with. Look me in the eye sir! Look me in the eye! No nonsense now, no equivocation, or it will go hard with you. It has been maintained by the learned counsel & with a great deal of satisfaction, that thus far we have been unable to produce any witness who saw the fatal shot fired. [Peterson shows concern, so does Laura's counsel, and everybody.] Look me in the eye sir. [Deliberately, Impressively] Now, Sir, you saw the shot fired! You start! You turn pale! From the moment of the homicide to the present time you have never mentioned in any conversation, that you saw the shot fired! Never hinted at it in your examination yesterday! Do you know sir? that this silence constitutes perjury? [Peterson starts] This is carrying friendship to a great length Mr. Peterson.

You also testified yesterday that you did not announce Col. Sellers & the other visitors at the time of the homicide. Is this true sir?

Peterson: Yes, sir—

D. Attorney: But you started towards the reception room to announce them, didn't you? Eh?

Peterson: Yes sir—but I turned away—I did not go in—

D. Attorney: Why didn't you go in John? Eh?

Peterson: I—I—

D. Attorney: You've got a sudden hitch in your tongue, but you looked in didn't you?

Peterson: [Hesitatingly] N—no, sir. I—I—

D. Attorney: So I thought myself. Did you write to anybody that night?

Peterson: I—I don't remember—no, sir. I did not write to anybody.

D. Attorney: Oh, you *didn't?* I thought maybe you did—didn't you write to your Mother? Eh?

Peterson: [With a start aside] Oh, this must be some lawyer's trick—. she *must* have burned the letter—I wrote her. [Aloud] No, sir. I didn't write to anyone!

D. Attorney: Mr. Peterson, is this port—folio yours?

Peterson: Yes, sir, it is one Miss Hawkins gave me, she often gave me books & encouraged me to educate myself.

D. Attorney: And all these papers & things are yours?

Peterson: Yes, sir.

D. Attorney: Somebody wrote a letter that night & dried it upon one of these blotting sheets. The closing lines may be easily read, they're upside down but a mirror will rectify that. [Takes hand mirror from table] Look me in the eye sir! Look me in the eye! See if you can recognize this—[Holds mirror before book & reads] "Heaven, forgive me I turned away too late—I saw Miss Hawkins kill him. Burn this letter. From your aff. Son—John Peterson."

Duffer: [Rises] Nonsense!—Nonsense! This is—

D. Attorney: Wait a moment & see! Is this your hand writing?

Peterson: [Now entirely demoralized] Oh, I have ruined her, I have destroyed her!

Duffer: [Rising & interrupting with bitter sarcasm] How charming this is! How melo—dramatic! how delightfully theatrical! Why it's like one of those sweet little juggling surprises that dramatists introduce to stir the souls of the pit with. Oh, *do* go on the stage with your looking glass & book—*don't* let such a little bit of clap-trap go to waste, I beseech you, for you only throw it away upon a grave & practical jury. [Sits down]

D. Attorney: [To Jury compassionately] Gentlemen this is a good soul, but he has his sore places like the rest of us. He once wrote a play, but I'll not allude to that, for I like to be charitable. [Turning to Peterson]—Is this your handwriting?

Peterson: Yes, sir.

D. Attorney: Then you *did* see Miss Hawkins kill Col. Selby? Eh?

Peterson: [Brokenly] Yes, sir. I did—

D. Attorney: That will do John! Take your seat!

Sellers: John, you played the devil with the whole thing!

Mr Duffer: Col. Mulberry Sellers, will take the stand. [Which he does with dignity] Col. Sellers, you entered upon the scene of the killing a moment after the fatal shot was fired?

Sellers: I did sir.

Duffer: At that time did the prisoner at the bar seem sane?

Sellers: *No*, Sir. She had the eye of a maniac, as I came through the hall, I heard a voice say something about—

D. Attorney: Well, never mind what you heard a voice say, answer the Gentleman's question—

Sellers: Yes, but I want to tell—

D. Attorney: Answer the Gentleman's question.

Sellers: [Earnestly] But it would lead to it—

D. Attorney: Never mind what it would lead to—answer his question.

Sellers: [Impatiently] I'm talking to that Gentleman. [Pointing to Duffer] I'm not talking to you.

Duffer: She seemed insane. How did she manifest it?

Sellers: She—said she was sorry she killed him. [Laughter in court]

D. Attorney: I should think so!

Sheriff: Order in the court.

Duffer: But did she rave?

Sellers: Rave? I never saw anything like it. She tried to kill herself twice, within ten minutes. We thought she would die, she's got heart disease. Yes sir, heart disease. [Sellers then turns to Jury & begins to talk, is stopped by sheriff's voice—Order in the Court.]

Duffer: She talked incoherently, did she?

Sellers: Why, you couldn't make one word out of two, but she never could have done it in her right mind—[Turns] Why Gentlemen of the Jury!

Sheriff: Attend to the court!

Duffer: Has she ever shown a tendency to insanity in former years?

Sellers: O, yes, sir. Frequently. Frequently. Habitually.

Duffer: What seemed to be the peculiar form of her mania?

Sellers: A desire to find her father—her other father—the author of her being.

Duffer: How did this usually affect her?

Sellers: Well, sir, in various ways. You know I said before, she never saw her father, but there were some letters left behind, which described him as a man with one eye & a wooden leg. Well whenever she saw a man with them—trademarks—as a body might say, it used to fill her with excitement, she could never look at a one eyed man without emotion & a one legged man used to set her in a perfect whirlment of joy, but if she happened to flush a stranger, with one eye & a game leg, she'd hound that cripple to the end of the earth, but what she brought him to cover, & made him show up. Why, sir, a sound man was a sorrow to her, to see the pain & sorrow depicted upon that benign countenance, when she looked upon a thoroughly sound man, was something awful to behold— but there was a charm in her gentle spirit over a green patch & a patent leg, that was beautiful to behold—

D. Attorney: Well, sir, never mind your green patches, & wooden legs. Am I to sit here all night, & be deluged with this torrent of intolerable rubbish—

Sellers: If you want to—

Duffer: That will do Col. Sellers, that will do! [To D. Attorney] Take the witness sir.

D. Attorney: [Rises, looks at Sellers, puts chair back.] Col. Sellers do you know the prisoner? [Sellers turns from him in contempt] Do you know Miss Laura Hawkins?

Sellers: That's a *pretty* question to ask me!

D. Attorney: Never mind the question, but answer it! Do you know Miss Hawkins?

Sellers: Do I *know* her? I known her ever since she was so high [putting hand two or three feet from floor]—I may be her *father* for all I know.

D. Attorney: Ha! Ha! Ha! You're not quite certain my dear Colonel— the fact of it is—your little gallantries have been so numerous, you—

Sellers: [Gravely & Impressively] Stop! sir. Stop! sir. That was a mere figure of speech, innocently uttered—don't you put a base construction upon it! It would not become you as a Gentleman to *do* it, it would not become me as a Gentleman to *permit* it sir!

Uncle Dan'l: [Among the visitors] O, Golly Ha! Ha! Ha! the old man had him—Whew—had him there—

Sheriff: Order in the court—sit down, sir!

D. Attorney: Col. Sellers, upon your entrance to the reception room in the Dilworthy Mansion, didn't you hear a voice say, I have killed the only man I ever loved?

Sellers: Yes, sir. I did, sir.

D. Attorney: Whose voice was it?

Sellers: It was Miss Laura Hawkins, but she didn't know what she was doing—[Turns to Jury]. Why Gentlemen—

Sheriff: Order in the Court! Order in the court!

D. Attorney: Now, Colonel, from the clear, coherent, & decided manner of that voice, don't you believe she knew—

Duffer: Oh, I protest sir—

D. Attorney: But we have a right to show—

Duffer: The learned counsel, under the shallow pretense—

D. Attorney: The learned counsel shall decide—[They both take up books & go up to Judge]. [Confusion in the court]

Sellers: [Turning to the Jury. Earnestly & persuasively.] Now, Gentlemen of the Jury. I know you can't find it in your hearts to bring her in guilty, she *never* could have done it in her sound mind! Why, she's an Angel, yes she is. She may be a little too proud & frisky for a regular old fashioned bible angel, but she's an angel—if you knew her as I do, if you'd carried her in your arms as I have, I know you'd say, Go, poor ruined heart, go poor desolate mind—[The Court has become still while the witness is speaking, the Judge & counsel look on him with surprise at this point].

Sheriff: *Order* in the court—

Sellers: And if you'll do as I tell you, you'll do right—

Sheriff: *Order* in the court.

Judge: The witness will confine his remarks to the answering of questions.

Sellers: Well, Judge, I'm not used to the forms of procedure of the courts in this section of Country, but out west sir, where the great American Eagle spreads its pinions over the Rocky Mountains & the Seere Nevada's—

Judge: There! There! sir that will do.

Sellers: Well there didn't happen to be any questions before the court at that moment, so I thought I would take advantage of the lull in the proceedings, to explain to the Jury, now if you will allow me sir—it won't take me long—Now my theory is this. [Turns to Jury & whispers]—[Confusion in the court] I've got one man there anyway—

Judge: Proceed Mr. Duffer—

Mr Duffer: That will do, Col. Sellers, you may take you seat.

Sellers: [Walks up to Judge] Judge, I mean no disrespect, but I don't think the Jury have had it explained to them fully—

Judge: Will you sit down sir? [Sellers subsides]

Sellers: [Aside & taking seat] I'll have a disagreement any—how—

D. Attorney: May it please the Court, & Gentlemen of the Jury. You have heard the evidence given here & you are now aware as I am, that there is not a shadow of a question but that the prisoner committed the highest crime known to the law! Murder. I entreat that you will bear in mind what I am about to say. You know that the American Criminal Jury system is Sneered at, is Jeered at, and referred to with boundless contempt. You know it is also said that no Man can take his place here as a Juror until he has proved to Court & Counsel that he reads neither books nor papers, that he has formed no opinion upon any subject, that he is totally incapable of forming an opinion, that his mind is filled with maudlin sentimentality, & his sympathies frame his verdict & not his intellect. And O Gentlemen I urge you, I implore you, I beseech you, to weigh the evidence given here, with inflexible justice & all mindful of the sacred oath you have taken, to award to this *red handed murderess* the doom, the *just doom*, her awful crime deserves. [Sits down]

Duffer: Gentlemen of the Jury, I will not insult you patience, your charity, or your generosity, by making a labored argument, to convince you of what is perfectly patent upon its face, viz that this poor injured girl—[Sellers: How kind & how graceful, so different from that grey headed old cuss.—meaning D. Attorney] in a fit of emotional insanity killed her destroyer. The law has no *right* & no *desire* to punish her *for* it. For the Law punishes only criminals of sound mind. I have not another word to say. [Sits down]

Sellers: There's no necessity for it. Allow me to congratulate you Mr. Duffer. [Shakes hands]

Judge: Gentlemen of the Jury! You have heard the evidence & the argument of Counsel. If you find that the prisoner was insane at the time of the killing, your verdict will be not guilty, but if you find that she was sane, then let the evidence determine the character of your verdict—You will now retire. [Exit Jury, in charge of sheriff. Sellers & the family go to Laura.]

Mrs Hawkins: My Child, my child. O, this awful suspense!

Laura: Cheer up, Mother darling. Let all be as God will. I have committed a great crime. I have repented—bitterly repented. I am ready to suffer.

Mrs Hawkins: O, my child, *do* not talk so! My heart is ready to break.

Sellers: There's no necessity of breaking your heart. [To Laura] Tomorrow we'll go away to Missouri & forget all about this disagreeable business. Cheer up, cheer up. That's a good girl. [Kisses Laura]

Laura: Ah, Father. I have so shamed the name you gave me. You were always so kind to me, & I have repaid you, by dishonoring you—you never can forgive me. I know you *never* can.

Hawkins: Forgive you, my darling? Forgive you! A Father's heart stands wide open to his erring child, always. And O, when this terrible day is over, we will go away, and find rest & peace, rest & peace, my Child—

Laura: Clay, my faithful brother, my old playmate in child-hood—let me feel the clasp of your hand. [Takes his hand] It gives me strength—it lifts up my whavering courage. I can wait now—Whatever may come. [Enter Jury & Sheriff—all take seats]

Judge: Gentlemen of the Jury! Look upon the prisoner—Prisoner look upon the Jury. [Laura rises] Gentlemen of the Jury have you agreed upon a verdict?

Foreman: We have.

Judge: What say you—Is the prisoner at the bar—Guilty or not Guilty?

Foreman: [After a pause] *Not Guilty.*

Tableau and Curtain

GROWING UP IN BERKELEY WITH
THE BOMB/ *Norman Lavers*

I cannot paint
What then I was
Wordsworth
"Tintern Abbey"

O N OUR VACATION IN the summer my father used to take us up to Blue Lakes in northern California. We'd leave Berkeley, drive out through Richmond, then stop at the end of the long line waiting for the ferry to San Rafael on the north side of the bay, so that we could continue our journey. It was a bottleneck in summer that has now been cured by the building of the San Rafael Bridge. But for my part, I loved the waiting in line, and I loved the ferry ride across the opaque green water of the bay. I imagined immense creatures swimming beneath, and I was fascinated by the curious fact that the water looked so warm and inviting though I knew, objectively, that it was cold and deadly.

This one time I remember, we were waiting in line and a freckle-faced, tow-headed kid about my age was going from car to car selling newspapers. My dad didn't want a paper, but he said to the kid, "I'll bet you a dime you don't know what the best city in the world is."

The kid said, "I do too. Oklahoma City." My dad said, "Oh heck, you win," and gave him a dime.

At that moment it came to me with the force of minor revelation (no doubt this is why the incident has stayed in my mind) that everyone thinks where they came from is the best place in the world. This was immediately followed by a second minor revelation: where I was growing up, Berkeley, California, U.S.A., 1940s, really was, arguably, objectively, by anyone's impartial analysis, the best place in the world.

No doubt like the paper boy I was somewhat blinded by loyalty and familiarity, but still, some fifty years later, I tend to hold to that belief. But I have had to amend it quite a bit. It was the best place to grow up if, like me, you were born around 1935, which is to say, too young for the Second World War or the Korean War, too old for Vietnam. If, like me, you happened to be a White Anglo-Saxo Protestant (though even that wouldn't have done much good if, like the paper boy, your face and accent gave you away as a dust-bowl Okie or Arkie). I remember—at the time it made no particular impression on me—my father going around to the neighbors on upper Euclid Avenue to get their signatures on a covenant not to sell their houses to minorities. After my mother divorced my father in 1949, she and I moved to a house in Park Hills, at the top of the Berkeley hills, on the edge of Tilden Park. We read the regulations for having a house within this somewhat exclusive subdivision: all houses will have peaked, shingle roofs, etc. etc., and, the owner agrees not to sell to Negroes or Jews. When this sort of restriction later was pronounced to be against the law, we received a new booklet of regulations, wherein this proviso was left intact and easily readable, but with a very thin pencil line drawn through it. I remember that Berkeley High School, when I went there, seemed to be about one-third white, one-third black and one-third Mexican, but it never once occurred to me that in P.E. class, on the days we swam in the school swimming pool, I never saw a black or a Mexican face. I only realized recently when I read in *Berkeley at War: The 1960s* (W.J. Rorabaugh, Oxford, 1989), that they were not allowed in the pool.

But if you fit into this now somewhat narrow category (and if, I may as well add, your daddy was fairly rich), and if, like me, at that time you had no concept, or even presentiment of social consciousness, then it could be argued that this was one of the finest places in the world to grow up. After all, America had come out of the Second World War the richest and most powerful country in the world. California was one of the richest and most powerful parts of America. The San Francisco Bay region, with its Mediterranean absence of season, with its pure blue North African skies, its oak-savannah hillsides, olive and dry-grass yellow in summer, bright with poppies and lupines in the wetter winters, was blessed with beauty and mildness of climate beyond compare.

Well, I admit the climate was, to me, something of a disappointment. In summer the fog came in at night and sometimes burned off in late morning, but it too often lingered until late afternoon, when it was time for the next night's fog to come in. I was one of those kids who brought home every snake or bug or spider. I kept them in jars with holes punched in the top. No animals would be stirring outside in such gloom. It dripped steadily off the eucalyptus trees in an oily rain staining the sides of the house and coating car windshields. I remember the depression of waking up in the morning in the middle of summer to the sound of the central heating coming on, the clicking of its expansion, the smell of dust burning off the furnace, and knowing there was no real purpose in getting out of bed.

But when the fog burned off early, the sun was always waiting behind it for a perfect day. Except for the fog, there was essentially no weather, no wind, no clouds, no storms in this mild desert, and when I could, I was out in it every second, especially after we moved to Park Hills, out walking in the large regional park that went along the tops of the Berkeley hills for miles. I knew every inch of every trail and came back in the evening with my clothes stained and stinking from the different aromatic shrubs of the high coastal chaparral I had pushed through, often with a new snake or lizard to build a cage for, a new giant waterbug to set up in an aquarium.

In the end I grew to appreciate even the fog. It figured in what was for me something like a religious ceremony. Here is what I sometimes did: In midsummer I would walk down the back side of the hill from my house into Tilden Park to Lake Anza, around to the other side of the lake and up the path along Wildcat Canyon Creek to the Botanical Garden, then skirt the edge of the golf course (considered one of the most beautiful in the world with its steep up-and-down fairways divided by rows of graceful eucalyptus trees, the live-oak encrusted hills of the park rising around it) and climb up out of the canyon to the top of the highest hill on the ridge, nearly 2,000 feet. To the west was a vista of the entire San Francisco Bay, the flat part of Berkeley before me, Berkeley Pier running out halfway across the bay, the Oakland Bay Bridge crossing over first to Yerba Buena Island, then to San Francisco, whose white buildings stood up in the clear air like a city in the *Arabian Nights*. To the north of The City, the orange-painted Golden Gate Bridge crossed over to Marin County, and Mount Tamalpais, the "Sleeping Lady," so named because the mass of the mountain resembled a recumbent body, with, at one end, an ample bosom rising up. Near the bridge was Alcatraz Island, the federal penitentiary, and to the right, Angel Island, and right off that the north end of the bay, and Richmond.

Beyond the bay, beyond the peninsula of San Francisco, out through the Golden Gate, was the Pacific Ocean. In summer the warm air over the cold currents produced constant fog, so that the ocean, beyond the gates, was solidly white with swirling clouds.

Behind me, where I stood, to the east, was first the valley of the San Pablo Dam, the watershed for the utility company that provided water for the region, and this was all wild, untouched country where no one was allowed to set foot, in order to keep the water pure, and beyond that Orinda and Walnut Creek and other towns of the interior valleys. The fog seldom went inland that far, so in summer they baked under the hot desert sun, temperatures over a hundred commonplace. As I stood there (I timed myself to arrive late in the afternoon), facing the Bay, I felt the hot-oven breath on my back from the interior valleys, and on my front a chill from the ocean fog, still thirty miles distant.

Then it happened. The heat in the valley would have been expanding the air all day long. The thinner, heated air rose, leaving a vacuum below, and the cool air from the Bay rushed in to fill the vacuum. You first felt the cool wind rushing toward you, chilling your sweating chest and face, while the furnace heat from the valley still warmed the back of your trousers and tee-shirt. Then you saw that the uprush of air from the Bay was pulling the fog behind it. The ocean fog was now a wall against The City, rising up like water in a basin, and the first bits spilled over Twin Peaks. A long arm of fog streamed in through the Golden Gate, rising up quickly, so that the tops of the two orange towers of the bridge alone remained in view. More fog was flowing into the north bay, and rising up Mount Tam. In the meantime the fog had spilled over the top of San Francisco itself and come pouring into the bay, which quickly filled with cotton batting, resembling the view of clouds from an airplane. The fog was quickly rising up, the well of the bay filling, Berkeley vanishing, the first thin wisps coming over you at eye level, the temperature dropping by degrees every minute.

Then you were engulfed in it, clammy and chill against your skin, and you hurried down the hill and the miles back to your house, to arrive before full opaque dripping darkness.

My grandfather was a painter who specialized in seascapes. He had built a small house right on the Bay in a little fishing village called Tiburón, over on the other side of Angel Island. My aunt Helen, his daughter, an old-maid schoolteacher, lived with him and, since he didn't sell his paintings, I suppose supported him. When I was little I often spent long periods of time there in the summer. I was up first thing in the morning, my aunt gave me breakfast, then I was gone with my fishing rod and bait and my lunch. I was up and down the rocky beaches all day long, investigating all the life crusted on the rocks, under the low-tide seaweed, in the tide pools or under the stones I rolled, feeding tiny crabs to giant sea anemones, watching the yellow jackets and tiny black Argentine ants fighting over smelly leftover bits of bait at the fishing areas. Sometimes the tiny ants, with the intelligence of wolves surrounding a giant moose or bison, or perhaps more like Pleistocene man surrounding a mammoth, would gather around a yellow jacket that was industriously cutting a section of rotten sardine to carry off, and seemingly at a signal, one ant would grab hold of each of the yellow jacket's six legs, and then, holding the wasp spread-eagled, each ant would hold onto the rock it was clinging to for dear life. The yellow jacket, suddenly realizing it was caught, would buzz its wings trying to take off, but it wouldn't be able to pull free, and it wouldn't be able to bring its powerful jaws or its deadly sting around to fight back. Now other ants would swarm over its body, and soon have the giant creature dismembered to carry back to the nest.

In the evening when I came back home, with my string of perch or jacksmelt or cabazone which I would gut and scale or skin, and which my aunt would cook up for me, the surface of my skin was so chilled from the hours of total absorption I had spent in the cool damp air along the edge of the sea that when my aunt put me into a bath, if she added even the tiniest most imperceptible amount of hot to the water it burned me, and even cold water from the tap was as hot as I could bear.

I'm just trying to give an inkling of how wonderful this growing up in the Bay Area was for me.

At some time somewhere someone brought me into the house to hear on the radio that an atom bomb had been dropped on Hiroshima. A day or so later, another was dropped on Nagasaki. Then, on another day, I was in the car with my aunt, and we were driving, probably, to Sausalito from the house in Tiburón to go grocery shopping, a view of the Bay and San Francisco ahead of us. It would have been in her neat little black '39 Plymouth. The radio was on and the program was interrupted to announce that the Japanese had surrendered and the war was over. Within seconds someone in San Francisco had sent a rocket high in the air. He must have had it set up for months or years waiting for the announcement. A minute later there was another interruption, another announcement: That was a mistake, the war is not over. I thought of the chagrin of the poor guy who had sent up his rocket. Then in another minute, a final announcement, Yes, the war is over.

That other war, the war that I grew up into manhood with, was about to begin, no doubt had already begun: The Cold War, that war in which Korea and even Vietnam were only minor blips, that war that governed the economics and politics and psychology of this country and, for that reason, of most of the world for the next fifty years. This is when The Bomb began to come into everyone's consciousness.

It was particularly in the 50s, those years we look back on as so innocent and charmed, that we worried about The Bomb. Here is how it affected me. I loved walking, and I had taken to walking everywhere. Almost daily I left my mother's house in Park Hills, walked over to Grizzly Peak Boulevard, then wound my way down Shasta, then down Euclid, to the north edge of the Berkeley campus, then on into town, either to visit friends, or more often, to go through the secondhand bookstores. I was almost always alone in those days (except for my wife now, I suppose I am essentially always alone still), walking, walking everywhere. Increasingly, I walked down into Berkeley at night, staying late, and walking back up the hills in the small hours, having the streets entirely to myself.

Sometimes, at one or two in the morning, coming up streets north of the campus, I heard the tapping of heels, and a young woman would be walking alone ahead of me. This was in the days before street violence was taken for granted, but still, it occurred to me that if she saw a lone man walking up quickly behind her, it might frighten her, so I turned back and went up another street instead.

But I am talking about The Bomb, and this is how it impinged on my consciousness. At a certain point in my walk down Shasta, which is the way I came down off the hill, I would come around a corner, and suddenly there was the whole basin of The Bay laid out before me, either in daylight drenched with clear sunlight, or at night even more beautiful, the intense black hole of The Bay encircled by its necklace of lights—the big yellow lights of the Bayshore Freeway on the Berkeley-Oakland side, other arterials around the bay, the blinking lights on top of the high pillars of the bridges, every street outlined like a spider web shining with droplets.

It was at this spot that it always occurred to me that I would be right here when it happened, the sudden dazzling dome of the nuclear explosion swelling from the center of the bay. At that point where the street curved, there was a concrete wall supporting it, and I always imagined to myself that I would duck behind that wall for shelter. In the extremest moments of my Bomb paranoia, I never imagined myself as perishing, but always as surviving marginally in the hills, a permanent exile from my paradise, avoiding contact with the invading Russian soldiers.

Before television was widespread we still had the Movietone between main features at the movies, where we saw, repeatedly, the annihilating flash of the bomb, followed by the roiling mushroom, over Eniwetok Atoll, and increasingly, in the Nevada or New Mexico desert. Eisenhower had come on the radio to publicly announce that there was absolutely no danger to citizens. We saw—an "exercise"—the soldiers with their steel helmets and full field packs, waiting in their trenches for the explosion, then, at a command, swarming out and charging into ground zero.

We began our Interstate system; the idea behind it was that with warning of an attack coming to one of our major cities, people would need to have a way of evacuating quickly. Buildings around the bay with deep basements were designated as bomb shelters, and placards were put up with the little propeller symbol of radiation, and the sign, "Fallout Shelter," so we would be able to find them quickly. People began building backyard bomb shelters. The going rate was $1500. A great debate started. If you built a shelter for yourself and your family, with supplies of food and water sufficient to get you through the two or three weeks you would need to wait underground before the radiation danger disappeared, what was your moral obligation to your neighbors, who had not taken provision for the future as you had? Did you have to let them in, even though that compromised your own survival? If they tried to get in by force, were you morally permitted to shoot them? In a widely printed public statement, a prominent religious leader announced that yes, it would be permissible to shoot your neighbors in order to preserve your own family.

A friend of mine told me, with only a slight touch of apologetic self-irony, that he had not gotten around to digging a bomb shelter yet, but he *had* bought a .22.

I was down in Los Angeles visiting my sister Viv, whose husband was a designer at Lockheed. She told me she had been at a Lockheed party and Kelly, the boss there at that time, had taken some of the wives aside and said the following: We know this for certain: The Russians are going to attack. Only, we don't know when. We know it will be within the next one or two years. We know it will probably be on a national holiday, because then the most people will be out on the road, and there will be the possibility for the most confusion. When it comes, if you survive the first blast, I want you to head for Tijuana any way you can.

My sister said, "What if, when it happens, I'm separated from my children." He looked her hard in the eyes: "Viv, make more babies."

Although this new, mortal ingredient had been added to my paradise, oddly, nothing changed externally. The light was the same (oh, perhaps there was beginning to be a smudge of smog in the bay off Oakland, but Oakland was a grimy place anyway). In fact something quite wonderful happened, making it, for the time, even better. In the small hours of the night I was walking through the trails in Tilden Park, and I came down off a hill and crossed a road. At that moment, as luck would have it, a park ranger came by in his pickup, caught me in his lights, and stopped. I came up to him, thinking I was going to have to answer some annoying questions about what I was doing there. The park, after all, closed at something like ten o'clock. But in fact when I said I was out looking for wildlife, he thought nothing was odd in that, and invited me to come along with him. He had a shotgun in the truck, and I was astonished to find, in this nature reserve, that he was shooting deer.

It seems the deer, overpopulated in the absence of predators, were getting into the botanical garden at night and devouring expensive species, so they were trying reduce their numbers. While we toured up and down the back roads, shotgun and jacklight at the ready, he told me a terrific story. In this innocent time that I am writing about, back when DDT was our helpful friend, and animals were divided into good and bad on the basis of whether we ate them (good) or they ate something we wanted to eat (bad), there was a bounty on mountain lions, fifty dollars for killing a male, sixty dollars for killing a female.

They were already pretty rare because of the constant shooting pressure, but a young male was spotted down by San Pablo. A posse was immediately mounted, horses, dogs, many gunners, and they took out after the animal. The park wardens learned that the lion was running towards Tilden Park. They saw it as the answer to their deer problem and were anxious to get it safely within their boundaries. So the man I was riding with said he waited at the park gates until the posse showed up. He stopped them and pointed to the sign by the entranceway: All dogs must be on a leash; all horses must remain on bridle paths; no guns or shooting were allowed. The very disgruntled posse turned around and went home.

The next morning while people were out playing golf, suddenly a mountain lion appeared on one of the fairways. The players froze, the animal froze. Then, in a panic, it bounded into the trees. But of course the line between the fairways was only about two trees deep, so it found itself immediately in the middle of the next fairway, with people standing and staring at it, so it bounded into the trees again, only to come out on still another fairway. Despite the fact of it being a large, dangerous-looking animal, people were rolling on the ground laughing.

That had been a few weeks back, and no one had seen it since. It not only had all of Tilden Park to wander in, but also the San Pablo Dam water company property east of the park, a huge tract of wild land abounding with prey, where no people were permitted, so they hoped it would stay in the area permanently.

From then on when I walked through the park, the big cat was always on my mind, and at times I thought I could almost sense his presence. Twice up on the steep hillsides, in fields grown up six feet high with light brush, I found places where he had dragged his kills, dried-out carcasses now, the meat eaten off the bones, and—the telltale sign of a mountain lion kill—the neck vertebrae dislocated. The lions jump on the back of their prey, and holding it with one massive paw, they use the other to bend the head up until the neck snaps.

Early one morning in dense fog, a great horned owl hooting overhead, I walked up the path behind Lake Anza toward the botanical garden, and a yearling deer was lying in the center of the path, head tipped back and neck broken, the flesh eaten off the back along the spine. It was all absolutely fresh, the deer's eyes staring. I had probably chased the lion off coming round the corner.

Another time, years later, I was on the north side of Jewel Lake (this was long before it was the special little fenced-off nature study area it is today) walking along the muddy margin, and I found a single, perfect pug mark. I measured four inches by four inches. The young male had grown to full maturity.

Those were all my encounters; I never saw the mountain lion, but how much it meant to me to have this bit of the real primal wildness on the edge of all that population density.

Of course it is now long gone, and the basin of the bay is a smog trap, and there is gridlock on the highways, and homeless people asking you for your change, and I would no longer walk the dark streets. I put this here, about the lion, to stress that it was an actual as well as a false paradise that is gone, that is on the wane worldwide. Those original Berkeleyans, who controlled the city government and the housing and the use of the high school swimming pool, have long since moved to Orinda or Lafayette or other places east of the Berkeley hills, and are now distressed to find the smog and traffic and drugs and house burglaries following them, so that they will have to move again and again. Because these urban problems are also symptoms of problems of their own making, of their exploitation of the paradise to satisfy their greed, and to keep as many others as possible from sharing it. And I share their guilt because I profited by their greed, in my blindness and naiveté colluded with them.

We all did our military service in those days. I enlisted for three years, RA, Regular Army. I went into the Army Security Agency, I studied Chinese at the Army Language School, I got top-secret clearance, I was in Korea working in radio-intercept observation posts along the DMZ and then worked in the National Security Agency when it opened in Maryland. It was easy getting clearance. After all, my mother worked at the Lawrence Radiation Lab in Berkeley. I was, like everyone I knew at that time, a staunch anti-communist. How slowly my attitudes turned around, how long I supported the war in Vietnam, and how painful it was for me to change. It seems to me still that it was easy for the younger people, the generation after mine, who had not grown up when I did. It was so effortless for them to be in the right, that they really did not deserve their good conscience.

I came back from the army and stayed in the Bay Area long enough to get an M.A. at San Francisco State. It was already seething with politics, premonitory of the Free Speech Movement that would start in another year or two in Berkeley. I watched it with interest, but bemusedly. I'm a loner, not a joiner, an observer, not an activist. The civil rights marches were going on in the South, and I read about them. I even knew people who had dropped everything to go down there, people I am so envious of today for having had that experience, for being able to say that they took part, that they knew to take part, in that decisive social action. Had I been deeply committed to the movement, I don't know if I would have had the courage to go. But the truth is, somehow it didn't touch me. I was on another planet.

That's not entirely true. There were counter currents, I was certainly becoming aware that there were oppressed people. Two incidents affected me more powerfully than I realized at the time: one was the Hungarian rebellion where young people fought with their hands against Soviet tanks. On the news a woman in Hungary was interviewed whose son told her he was going off to fight, and he and she both knew it was to his death—and she let him go. It made me realize in the most immediate way that some things were bigger than a person's life, and that it was only the accident of my being born here rather than there that spared me from having to make the kinds of decisions these people were making. And the other event, which in my mind is always associated with it, perhaps because it was close together in time, took place in this country: the black children attempting to go to a segregated white school in Little Rock. A lone little black girl, surrounded by jeering and spitting whites, their faces contorted and made ugly by their hatred. She is standing facing a soldier, one of the Arkansas National Guard, who is brandishing his rifle-mounted bayonet at her, to stop her from entering the school. Over these years I am writing about, these images continued sinking in deeper and deeper. They continue to haunt me now almost forty years later.

There is one more: Alabama governor George Wallace had made headlines around the country by stating that he was personally going to stand in the doorway and deny entrance to some black students who were attempting to integrate a school in his state. There was a court order saying they could enter. Push was going to come to shove and all the press was there to cover the event.

I was walking down University Avenue in Berkeley. It was a quiet afternoon, the sidewalk empty, almost no traffic on the street. Suddenly a car on the other side of the street veered over to my side, pulled up next to me. A young black guy inside rolled down the window. I had never seen him before, nor he me. His face had a relieved smile on it.

"The governor's backed down," he said. "He let them go in."

We sat together in his car and listened to the event on his radio, sharing that moment of history together.

I left the Bay Area around that time and have never lived there again, though I go back often enough to visit family briefly. It's since I left in the early '60s, in the main, that it has become what it is famous for today, a cradle for protest, a mecca for dissidents and hippies and gays. People don't believe me when I say how right-wing Berkeley was, how racist, how narrow, how rigidly controlled the politics, how important fraternities and football were, how the blacks were kept in their certain set of streets, the Mexicans in theirs, the Okies in theirs.

What is even harder to say is, if you had the right color skin to be allowed to use the school swimming pool, if you had the right income and religion to live up in the hills, how nice Berkeley was with its small locally owned shops, with its uncrowded streets and smog-free air, with its absence of industry (all zoned out to Emeryville), with its nonexistence of drugs or burglaries or muggings, with its teen-aged gangs who had major confrontations and gave each other black eyes and bloody noses. I know now that my innocence was a blindness, that many things that exist now in the open existed then out of sight, or at any rate, out of my sight, that (this also comes from reading *Berkeley at War*) at the same time I was dreaming my way through Berkeley High, going to proms and sneaking into Cal football games on Saturday afternoons, Bobby Seale, later a founder of the Black Panthers, was also going to Berkeley High, but he was feeling disenfranchised, he was dropping out and living on the streets, he was reading Frantz Fanon.

So the innocence of the 50s, as everyone now knows, was a privileged innocence, an innocence based on blindness. The secret guilt of my class, secret even from me, projected itself up from our unconscious in the form of our fear of The Bomb. Maybe the threat of The Bomb was real and maybe it wasn't. But I am only talking about the fear, and the fear was the fear that those who have have of those who don't.

There was a specific moment, I begin to think in retrospect, when my re-education reached critical mass, which is to say, the moment that my guilt (disguised to me as bomb fear) began to become conscious. Classic Freudian theory tells us that when repressed material is brought to the surface, its hidden, encoded, neurotic expression disappears.

For some time, at the height of the bomb fear, I had been somberly telling people that, Yes, we knew the attack was coming, but we didn't know when. We only knew that it would probably be on a national holiday, because then the most people would be out on the road, and there would be the possibility for the most confusion.

I was again down visiting my sister Viv in LA, maintaining to all comers my grim prognostication. One day Viv said they had a friend who was coming over to visit, and she was looking forward to introducing him to me, because, like me, he was a terrific, in fact, a prize-winning debater, and it would be fun to get us together.

I don't know what I expected. What should a champion debater be like? Intense, intellectual, aggressive, some combination of these. After all, that's how I was. But this guy when he came was small, rather soft looking, soft spoken, and utterly ordinary.

"Oh, hi," he said, when I came in the room. (He had my sister's kids sitting on either side of him.) "Viv says you think there's going to be a nuclear attack."

"Yes," I said.

He looked at me with friendly curiosity.

"Do you really believe it'll happen?" he asked.

It was only days, or perhaps weeks later that it suddenly dawned on me why he was such a good debater. His gentle appearance, his innocent, non-confrontational question, had completely disarmed me. I hadn't even realized I was in a debate. If he had said Why will it happen? I would have given him my pat arguments. Instead, his question made me look inside myself.

I was so surprised by what I found, that I looked again.

"Well," I said. "Come to think of it, I guess I really don't."

And I no longer did.

Norman Lavers, a past winner of *MR*'s William Peden Prize, is this year's recipient of the Porter Prize for Excellence in Literature and is the new editor of the *Kansas Quarterly/Arkansas Review*.

THE APPROACH OF WAR / *E.C. Hinsey*

That morning, daylight was the same.
   Everyday rituals, observed by no one,
  left the bedroom door open as a jaw in sleep.
The faucet's three-four time went unnoticed.

At midday, a ragged curtain shifted in the breeze.
   The paper's checkered voice quietly yellowed.
When afternoon arrived, there was soot in the air,
and birds stayed nested in the dark, thatched groves.

Across an open field, a querulous voice called once
   and received its answer.
The road was empty. A car, wrapped in dust,
swept the lane, vanished.

The willows were still. A door mated a latch.
   At dusk the smell of pears rose,
and a mist trawled the lake.
A match was cupped under the dome of a palm.

Night, not yet soiled, made its way across
   the lake and into the arms of branches.

THE DISASTERS OF WAR, SPAIN, 1810
/ E.C. Hinsey

After Goya

The fires were low, and because it was
　　night, the engine of folly had taken
　　　　to flight for a time. I walked the rows,
　　roaming as one would a ruined place,

my lantern not Diogenes', but seeking
　　a recognizable face among the carnage.
　　　　My lamp swung low, a censer of light.
　　I stopped, for a hand reached up, lit

for a moment in its dreaming. What
　　my hand touched I didn't know—I
　　　　pieced through bodies as a river goes,
　　threading myself, as if around the rocks:

dark bodies lay like slate in that empty
　　cleft of night. All the world's passion
　　　　spent, left to rot on the ground. Day alone
　　would see me fallen. There perhaps I

lay with you, as only my empty lantern
　　knew, casting its last flame on your back,
　　　　your hands entwined, your jaw gone slack—
　　praying face down in the mud.

　　　Para eso habeis nacido
　　　(For that you were born.)

ON A VISIT TO BUDAPEST / *E.C. Hinsey*

One cannot live without love—this statement
so simple, so mundane, came to me in that
city where we roamed around the baths. I
hadn't known it until the tilt of your head,
suddenly, in shadow, confirmed all I knew,
and though my children and husband waited
I let you lay me down while the wind berated
the dry leaves overhead. What I hadn't
known was how, at forty, the heart can
reanimate—and how plans, even one's
own flesh can drift, suddenly out of focus,
seen from the wrong end of a telescope.
When I returned, my husband hadn't noticed.
The children looked up from their play
murmuring their own eccentricities.
I thought about you night and day, until
it seemed I would burst with words unsaid,
unraged. Daylight transfigured all I knew.
Every motion seemed absurd—clothes
packed in trunks seemed like funeral chests
where once I lay down and gave myself away.
I'm not the same as I was at twenty-two,
yet once I was glad to walk the streets
at night and listen to how dawn would light
on my sill. I hear it still, but before today it
was the far-off echo of a voice faded
behind a wall, distance claiming its toll.
If life is hazardous, this the greatest one of all:
the heart cannot be led like a dog
but rises up, and seeks its goal.

NIGHT IN CLAMART / *E.C. Hinsey*

Marina Tsvetayeva, 1933

As if the first night,
hyacinths are speaking
color to the darkness.

As when you walked,
head down, head hung
with stars,

along roads written
as afterthoughts,
threatened with dissolution

by dirty rains.
Contretemps your lot,
passion its antidote.

The empty roads
tonight look
for your shadow,

but you are neither
form nor voice,
unable to describe

their makeshift rifts,
their part in the joke
loss and circumstance

played on you. If one
could call to you tonight!
Tell you it's all beginning,

the rivers starting again
from their sources, your
native homes, Moscow,

Prague, moving like
bridge ice into water.
For a moment there

is laughter, and the
moon rises like a kite
on its narrow string.

Only time betrayed
you, gutting you of
all you had, making you

ring out your sorrowful
notes, in the dark of night
and with no goodbye.

THE ROMAN ARBOR / *E.C. Hinsey*

Suddenly you felt it. And under the white
eye of afternoon, you turned

but could see nothing. Water flowed from
the mouths of the stone heads,

that hung, as if sacrificed, above their basins
in the trellised garden. You caught,

in an alcove of green, the quick movement
of a lizard as it traced the sandal

of a departed goddess. The garden was so still
that, apart from the shifting water,

you imagined sound had refused refuge there,
preferring to venture out towards

where the islands broke the authority of the
shoreline. Your calm was restored.

So when you met, face to face between the
columns, you were not prepared—

he stood greater than you, his stone locks
worn smooth as the tide's back,

his breast four times the hand's compass.
Breathless before his bulk, you

failed to notice that afternoon was gaining
territory. Then, slowly, under

the heat, a thought crept along the stone sills,
leaving behind a thin trail of grief.

Who is not like him—you asked—your words
  sifting in the striated light,

and turning as the sand lifted once in
  the hot breeze, you said:

Who is not a witness of ruined places?

DEATH OF THE TYRANT / *E.C. Hinsey*

One day, like hard October frost, he came to them,
though it took time for each to adapt.

Sour-faced drummers rattled their sticks in the square,
    while the birds left their nests, darkening
    the sky with their departure.

    Grains hardened on the staff.

The city soon sagged under the weight of days.
Passion and language were bent on the wheel:

seasons held down by the hand of function
    bore neither fruit nor folly. The tyrant
    was familiar by then,

    a family man.

He could be seen walking his dogs on Sunday
afternoons. And each January he let flow

a black ribbon of words from the podium.
    Since the hourglass had been destroyed,
    time ceased. At night

    there was a strange

calm, and all the animals that might have
bayed, one day simply disappeared—

followed by fountain pens, handkerchiefs
    and bread.
    Dawn was grey as cement.

    But silent as rust breeding

came the day when the south wind picked up
the paper in its mouth.

The soup suddenly boiled on the stoves.
    And bodies in uniform floated
    down the river like light barges.

    Once again sundials

cast their angles, and though silent,
the birds returned

perching above the castle like sentinels.
    A fire flared and the flames
    spoke in tongues.

    Seized with anxiety,

the city awaited the news. But after
the white bodies of saints had

risen from their graves, some secretly
    wept. Morning had cleared
    their downcast eyes, accustomed

    so long to partial sight:

their city which once boasted gold-faced
towers, cerulean-tipped flowers and

resplendent leaves—now lay before them
    like abolished tender, and they
    stared like those before

    the gates of hell.

THE JUMPING FIGURE / *E.C. Hinsey*

After months of public assurance that there would be no barrier built
between East and West Berlin, on the morning of August 13, 1961, the
first barbed wire was erected; in the following weeks, doors and
windows of apartments facing West Berlin were sealed.

All the day I have heard the sirens calling,
confiding to the distance a suffering
which moves each moment closer. Here among
familiar things, I hesitate before
my task: I am the figure in the clock
that hourly appears on the ledge, then
retreats from that beleaguered edge into
the close and shuttered dark. If I falter
it's that the past holds me so, in these rooms
where each night I have laid my
head—fatigued by choices I didn't make—
on linen white and neatly kept, yet soiled
by dreams of those once left for dead along
the routes that greatness took. And now as if
again disgraced, tanks move slowly through the
dust that's had barely fifteen years to rest.
Patience had been my guiding star. But can
I say I didn't choose to feel a certain
ecstasy in that first, long-ago spring, or feel
my girlhood bloom under the voices of furious
power? Then, when life was out of doors, one
waited in white under the linden trees,
as if the future too would arrive, swept
with the rest down the avenue.
                                        Now I'm
fitted like a fixture in this room.
After the war, the days that followed
seemed like time scattered on barren ground—
I walked alone bereft, as light cut through
the buildings with mirages. I was nineteen.
The year that might have been my glory
I passed bricks hand over hand, and watched
as birds rose from the ruins. So dreadful were

the deprivations, as the clouds moved in
vague formations, one almost hoped therein
for some redemption. Today, again displaced,
as if my body has been pledged to a dynasty
perched a third time on the edge:
I am left to survey the fall.
                                    But why
think now of such things? It's just that faces
in this room profess a perfect innocence—
the photographs lean in like a pious chorus
exacting these ultimate confessions.
Below a crowd stretches a cloth, as if
to define the territory of my absolution.
                                    I know
I have not grasped the nature of things,
but remember how velocity adds its hand
to that which drops from a height—
and know enough to fear the peace of those
who've missed the net: for as their faces
were free, their limbs were grasped
in such calligrams of despair. Through
my door I hear the sounds of those
who've come to seal my fate; held still by
the hands of doubt, I've let my body lean out:
I must accept the path my feet dictate.

E.C. **Hinsey's** book *Cities of Memory* was selected for the 1995 Yale Series of Younger Poets and will be published in the spring of 1996.

BOX SEATS/ *Tim Tomlinson*

T HE FIRST THING THAT got his father angry was the men's room.

"Christ," he said, grimacing. "Don't touch a thing." From a dispenser he yanked a handful of paper towels and wrapped them around his fists.

"I don't have to go," Cliff said. That was almost true. Before the inning had ended, Cliff tried to tell his father he didn't need to go urgently. What he did need urgently was Roger Maris's autograph. Roger Maris had hit sixty-one home runs. He broke Babe Ruth's record. That's why, before the game, when Roger Maris stood less than two feet away, Cliff had been too tongue-tied to ask. But he'd brought along his glove, and they had seats, box seats against the wall on the right field line, where Roger Maris played, and where he liked to hit his home runs. Cliff thought he might catch a home run. When he did he'd shout, "Mr. Maris, it's my birthday! I'm seven. Could you please sign my ball?" Would it be a lie to say it was his birthday? This trip was a birthday present, but his real birthday wasn't until four days away.

Now, in the men's room, with the Yankees coming up, Cliff feared he'd miss a second chance.

"Hey," his father said, "I'm not gonna tell you again."

"But I don't have to. I went before we left."

"That was three hours ago. It's the fourth inning now."

Actually, it was the third inning, the bottom of the third, but Cliff didn't correct him. His father hated to be corrected. He hated baseball, which to Cliff was like hating ice cream.

"Come on." Cliff's father kicked open a stall. His loafer left a black scuff on the door. The loafers were shiny new, a gift from Cliff's mother on their last anniversary, their tenth.

"Just go ahead?" Cliff asked him.

"Just go ahead," his father said.

Cliff slid past him, fingering the zipper of his suit pants.

"Don't touch anything," his father reminded him. "And watch your sleeves. You're wearing a white shirt."

Inside the stall, Cliff ran through the list of things he planned to do someday, all things his father hated: drag his sleeve through gravy, swallow without chewing, keep the fork in his left hand, play with his food, play with himself, make noise with his straw, say yeah, not watch his tone, walk across the lawn, litter, ignore injustice, make fun of retarded people, laugh at Negroes, skip sit-ups, overeat, get fat, enter the house without wiping his feet, go barefoot, put his hands on the walls, leave the bed unmade, the lights on, the door unlocked, talk back, hold the refrigerator door open.

Cliff's father's fingers dangled over the top of the stall door, a paper towel separating their flesh from the door's bacteria. Below the door, his loafers were spotless as a new driveway. He gently slid one foot back and forth along a loafer's tongue. His father's feet frequently itched, or burned, or throbbed, but in his usual shoes he couldn't relieve them. His usual shoes, the ones that he wore to climb lighting poles for LILCO, were work boots, or "boondockers," all brown, all with laces that tied above the ankle. From the moment he put them on before work until his lunch break, then from lunch till he got home, his feet tormented him without relief. That's why Cliff's mother had chosen loafers. Also because Cliff's mother thought his father needed to get more stylish, and the black slip-ons, she'd said, would go well with his new cigarettes. He'd changed from Marlboros, which had brown bands at one end of the white barrel, to Parliaments, which were all white and had a recessed filter. All-white cigarettes were more dressy. Cliff's mother smoked all-whites, Chesterfields. Chesterfields came with coupons but no filters. For their anniversary Cliff's father had given her a lighter. Her initials, JCF, for Jacqueline Capello Foote, were engraved inside a diamond-shaped box.

When it was clear that the loafers were not moving until Cliff had peed, Cliff said, "What about my aim?"

Sometimes at restaurants his father came into toilet stalls with him and held him, helped him with his aim. This was different, this was Yankee Stadium.

"Aim like I taught you, but don't worry if you go all over the seat."

Cliff looked at the seat. He wouldn't have been the first.

When he was little Cliff sometimes peed with his father. Those were tense sessions. Against the thunder of his father's stream, Cliff produced mere trickles, even after sixteen-ounce bottles of deposit Coke. His father taught Cliff how to aim, not relaxed in the hips with a careless dangle, like he did, but with a twofingered pinch at the base of the nozzle, the way you held a hose. And he taught him how to shake off, twice, sharply, with conviction. Now, if Cliff peed with anyone, it was with Wally, his brother. They weren't allowed to play while peeing, but they did anyway. They slashed at each other's stream in a game they called "crossing swords."

"Where are you gonna go?" Cliff asked.

"I'll be right here," his father said, "pissing in the sink."

Cliff loved it when his father talked like that, with curses. It was a nervous time when he did it, sometimes the curses were aimed at him, or at Wally, or at their mother, or sometimes all three of them. But when they were aimed at other things, like dirt, relatives, or at other drivers, like this morning when they drove into the stadium, they were partially shouted because he was mad, and partially shouted because he knew that Cliff and Wally would laugh.

At drivers with glasses he'd shouted, "You four-eyed asshole!"

On Jericho Turnpike he retaliated against drivers who may or may not have cut him off by cutting them off. In the rearview mirror their cars jerked and swerved while he watched, laughing.

"I wish you wouldn't do that," Cliff's mother said, lighting a Chesterfield with her anniversary lighter, her eyes fixed on the passing roadside. "You give them the wrong idea."

"It's these new slip-ons," he said, winking at the boys in the back. "They slip right off the gas."

"My Aunt Tilly," she said.

In Flushing, where the Grand Central Parkway forked off the Interborough Parkway, a driver in a Volkswagen signaled right but eased left. "You double-chinned pygmy!" he shouted, leaning on the horn.

It was funny to hear the curses, but even funnier when the person turned and actually had the attribute their father had mentioned. How could he see so far, Cliff wondered. It made him giddy, until he reached the point where his laughter became a series of scratchy clicks. Sometimes he had to fight for his breath.

Cliff's mother didn't like those scenes, although in Cliff's mind they were better than having the yelling directed at them. Cliff pictured her now, disapproving of his father making him laugh by saying bad things, wrong things. His father was funnier that way, funnier than his mother. His mother was safer.

Cliff thrust his pelvis forward, aimed with both hands, and waited for the pee. While he waited he looked around. It was dirty, his father was right. The wet floor was dotted by cigarette butts burst open from moisture. The toilet seat was stained a color that Cliff hoped was rust but looked disgustingly like something else. A weird scrawl covered the wall, a kind of writing Cliff couldn't understand, although he'd been the best reader in the first grade and expected to be the best in the second, which started in four days, exactly on his birthday. Wally's birthday had been the week before. He'd turned nine.

"You finished in there?" his father called. "I don't hear nothing."

"It's still coming," Cliff said.

Cliff was trying to go, was in a hurry to go. He wanted to rush back to the box seats. Earlier, Roger Maris had come right up to them. He reached over the wall, the wall that separated home runs from outs. He wore pinstripes, the home uniform, with short sleeves. His arms were like Cliff's father's arms, a network of taut ropes, alternately swelling and relaxing as he signed baseballs for the boys sitting alongside Cliff. He spoke to them, softly. They were older, twelve, maybe, or thirteen. They wore warm-up jackets with real numbers. When he finished, he looked at Cliff. Cliff had a baseball and a pen, but he couldn't raise his arms, and his tongue froze stiff as a creamsicle. Maybe that was the first thing that got his father angry. Why? Was it because he and Wally were too shy? Or was it because they looked at Roger Maris some way they never looked at their father? Sometimes it was hard to tell what made Cliff's father angry. Sometimes he was angry all the time, like Cliff's mother.

Cliff tried to forget about his hurry, he knew that hurrying only made it last longer. At home he could turn on the water if he couldn't pee, that could make it go faster. Away from home he needed to think good thoughts, neutral thoughts. He thought about running through the woods with his German shepherd, Wolf. He thought about Roger Maris. His father hated Roger Maris. His father thought Mickey Mantle, not Roger Maris, should have broken Babe Ruth's record. But he hated Mickey Mantle, too. Mickey Mantle didn't work hard enough. Nobody did, according to Cliff's father.

Cliff decided to think about things that had no connection to his father. Dirt. This stall, where everything was dirty or damaged. The toilet paper dispenser looked like an upside-down napkin holder in a diner, a stainless steel cover with black sides. It was big enough for two rolls of toilet paper but the roller on one side was bent in the middle as if it had been hit by a hammer. The other side held a roll, but that roll was shredded and scored with holes and gashes as if it had been raked by a saw. Part of it had been set on fire, the flames leaving iridescent teardrops on the silver, blistering the green paint. Cliff picked at a charred flake and his finger blackened.

He wiped the smudge on the toilet paper, then picked at another flake. But this flake wasn't a flake, it was the actual metal of the stall. Cliff fingered around it and discovered it was a hole, the metal bent back jaggedly as though it had been pried with a can opener. The hole had an odd circular shape, and was the size of a half dollar. He leaned a little closer. What would a hole be doing in the wall, he wondered. He wanted to stick his finger into it, to see if it went to the other side. How funny it would look to see a finger snaking out like a worm. But he remembered his father's warning: don't touch anything. This one time he could see why. Cliff's father and mother had unusual standards for hygiene and cleanliness. By the first grade, when he began visiting other people's houses, Cliff learned that most of those standards were excessive. "How did she keep her kitchen?" his mother would ask. "Did you touch anything in the bathroom?" his father would ask. "Were there fresh towels?" But this stall was unquestionably and by anyone's standards dirty. Still, could you actually touch a hole? Technically, if it was a hole, he wouldn't be touching anything and, therefore, he wouldn't be disobeying any command.

Cliff watched where his aim was, making sure that when the pee came it would reach the general vicinity of the toilet, and leaned forward to inspect the hole. When his eye reached hole level, he noticed something that looked like an eye on the other side. Was it a mirror? He leaned closer, and the eye was an eye! The eye of an older man, a man much older than his father. It was behind one thick lens, magnified like an insect in a paperweight, and was surrounded by a heavy black frame. It winked. The head behind it nodded.

Cliff shot back up to attention, his heart thumping.

"Dad," he said.

"You finished?"

He looked back at the hole, where now a dim shaft of light speared through.

"Yeah," he said.

The door swung open, his father's fingers protected by towels.

"Don't say yeah," his father said. "How come I didn't hear nothing?" He tried to see over Cliff's shoulder into the toilet.

Cliff shrugged and zippered up. He could still feel his heart thumping. What had happened? Could he tell his father? Would the man get in trouble for looking at Cliff? Would Cliff get in trouble for having leaned over to look himself? How long would that prevent them from getting back to the game?

"I had good aim." He blocked his father's view and quickly took his hand. The lie worked.

Cliff didn't like to lie, no matter how good he'd become at it. Lying separated Cliff from his father, who never lied, who hated liars, and who frequently reminded Cliff and Wally that liars had no honor. Lying was sinful, too. That's what they taught Cliff in Catechism. But the guy who wrote the Catechism didn't grow up with Cliff's father. If he had, he would have appreciated that it was often necessary to lie. Because it was also necessary—in fact it was commanded—that one obey one's father and mother. Cliff's father had taught him never to be a quitter, and never to let his friends, or his team down. But in order to carry out that command, Cliff often had to lie.

"Did you remember to water the hedges?" his father would ask.

"Yes," Cliff would lie.

"Did you remember to do your sit-ups?"

"Yes," Cliff would lie.

Cliff lied because he didn't want to be punished. He didn't want to be punished because then he wouldn't be able to play. If he wasn't able to play, he would be letting his team down— his baseball team, his football team—and that would be a direct violation of a commandment, which was closer to a mortal sin (it could even be a mortal sin) than the lesser "white" lie. White lies were venial sins.

Cliff understood his lies to be lies, and he lived with them. At first, that vast accrual of lies had been difficult to accomodate. He thought that lies were to the soul what cigarettes were to the lungs; the more you smoked the blacker they got. But Cliff had grown comfortable living with paradoxes. Black lungs. A stained soul. He hated his father, he loved his father. He wanted to kill his father viciously, he missed his father fiercely.

"Now come on, let's wash your hands."

He held the stall door for Cliff, then followed him to the sinks. Like a victim in a stick-up, Cliff raised his hands above his head. His father unbuttoned the cuffs on his sleeves and snapped them back three times, sharply, with no wrinkles. When they were little, he'd made a game of it. "This is the way the pirates rolled up their sleeves," he told Cliff and Wally. Then he rolled them so tight it looked like the sleeves came off a machine.

There were about twenty sinks, only two in use, one by a black man with a toothpick in his teeth.

"Is that Elston Howard?" Cliff asked his father. Elston Howard, one of the few black Yankees, hadn't been in the line-up. Instead, they had Yogi Berra behind the plate.

His father squeezed his arm.

The black man looked over. "Hey, little slugger," he said, tonguing the toothpick, "who you put your money on?"

Cliff looked at his father, and his father nodded.

"We got box seats," Cliff told the man. "In right field."

"Right field," the black man repeated, then whistled. He was large chested and wide-eyed, the whites as red as cough syrup. His powder blue hat seemed a size too small. And his brown pants, while creased and cuffed, seemed to be for play. At the seat and pockets, they shone from wear. One knee was torn, the other patched. He wore sneakers.

Cliff wore a suit and a clip-on tie. The suit, from Robert Hall, was midnight blue with faint red stripes. He'd worn it once before, on the day he'd received Holy Communion. Afterwards, he went home and tried to get the suit dirty. He rolled around on the worn-out patch of lawn that in his backyard stood for second base, but his mother had caught him. He was not allowed outside for the rest of that weekend. Holy Communion was on a Saturday.

His father and Wally wore suits, too. His father's was black. His tie, a real tie, was blue. The blue picked up his eyes, Cliff's mother had said. Wally's suit was plaid. First Wally and Cliff had complained about wearing suits at all. They claimed it was stupid to wear suits to a ballgame, and it was especially unfair on their birthdays. But their father had insisted. "We're going out as a family, and when we go out as a family your mother likes to get dressed." When their mother was invoked as the reason for something, there was no arguing, and they knew it. So they fought between themselves over whose suit looked stupider. Maybe that was the first thing that got his father angry.

The black man backed away from the sinks, his hands dripping. "Well you all watch out for line drives now. Them Tigers know how to pull the ball." At the towel dispenser he flicked water from his hands against the wall, then pulled down several paper towels. "You bring your glove?"

"Yeah," Cliff said, then cringed, but his father hadn't heard. His attention was fixed on the black man, who dropped his towels on the floor. His father's lip curled and he shook his head.

"If I catch one," Cliff asked the black man, "would Roger Maris still sign it?"

"Maybe, slugger, if you ask him nice. Yo Dad," the black man said, tapping two fingers against his lips, "you got a smoke?"

His father said, "I don't smoke."

The black man eyeballed Cliff's father, then nodded. "I hear you." He winked at Cliff as he left.

Cliff looked up from the sink. "You smoke," he told his father.

"Come on, watch your sleeves," his father said, still shaking his head. It was as if the towels the black man had dropped on the floor had become super-powerful magnets and his father's eyes paper clips. "Filthy black bastard," he muttered.

He reached across Cliff and turned on the water, his fingers still protected by towels.

"What's he mean, pull the ball?" Cliff asked.

In the corridors outside the men's room, fans scurried busily to and fro like ants. Everyone had places to go, things to do— even people in line, at souvenir stands, scorecard wagons, hot dog counters. Some left their place in line to peek into the ramps leading to their seats and the field. When they had their Cokes or their peanuts, they hustled back inside like workers returning to the nest with inchworms or pieces of leaf. It was always with regret that Cliff's father destroyed ant nests in their backyard. Cliff's father admired ants, their focus, their sacrifice, their unswerving sense of purpose. Cliff admired them, too, but he didn't think he'd make a good one. If he was an ant, he thought, he'd probably eat the inchworm himself, and if he had to carry back a leaf, he'd select a light one.

"You want to get a hot dog?" Cliff's father asked him.

Cliff shrugged.

"Come on, get a hot dog," his father said.

"I don't want one."

"But you love hot dogs."

"I'm not hungry," Cliff said.

"When did that ever stop you?" His father led him toward the counter where men wore paper caps that looked like battleships without the guns. The hot dogs nearest the counterman were brown. The ones in the middle reddened and fattened. At the back they looked cold, pink and thin.

"What do you want, a long one?"

A cheer rose up from the field. Cliff pictured Roger Maris leaping into the stands, into the right field seats, their seats, his seat, and stealing what would have been a Tiger home run. He pictured Roger Maris holding up the stolen home run, then signing it, then handing it to one of the boys in the warm-up jackets, or worse, to Wally.

"Can't we get one back at the seats?"

Cliff's father ordered two.

"They're fresher here," his father said. He called over the counter. "Can you stick a candle in it? It's his birthday." He palmed Cliff's brush cut.

The man looked over his shoulder. "What is he, thirteen?" He winked at Cliff's father. Hair grew out of his nose. If he was a driver, what would Cliff's father call him? Pigtail Puss?

With crusty buns, the nose-hair man squeezed hot dogs off a long fork, then placed them in a cardboard box. He slid the box across the counter to Cliff's father and picked up the bill Cliff's father had laid there.

"Answer him," his father said. "Tell him how old you are."

"Seven," Cliff said.

"Seven!" the man repeated. "He must eat a lot of Wheaties."

He came back with change. "Who's your favorite Yankee?" he asked.

"Ralph Houk," Cliff said.

"Ralph Houk?" the counterman said. "The manager?" He didn't know if he was being kidded, and he looked to Cliff's father for a clue. But Cliff's father only knew the names of the famous Yankees. Mickey Mantle, Roger Maris, Whitey Ford. There were so many others. Clete Boyer, Moose Skowron, Johnny Blanchard. He couldn't know that Cliff had just been disrespectful.

His father asked for mustard and relish and the man pointed to a counter off to the side.

"I don't like mustard," Cliff said.

"You love mustard," his father told him.

That was true. He was hoping his father wouldn't remember.

"Come on." He held the box of hot dogs in one palm, and led Cliff toward the condiment counter with the other. "This is Gulden's. Not that French crap."

He ran a plastic fork through a silver tray filled with relish. "You want some snot?" he said. He was trying to make Cliff laugh, so Cliff laughed. But more cheers erupted from the field and Cliff was getting edgy.

The mustard came in giant plastic jars, taller than half-gallons of milk. It was more mustard than Cliff had ever seen. Somehow, that much of it in one container made it less appealing. On top the jars had pumps that you had to press down like Bosco. Cliff's father lifted him from the waist so he could press one.

"Wait a second," he told Cliff, then wrapped a napkin around Cliff's fingers. Crusty mustard droppings streaked the jar like bird dob on a lighting pole.

Cliff pressed. Mustard blurted out, much more than he expected.

"Be careful," his father told him.

Cliff took a bite. A glob of mustard edged over the side of the bun. It splotched onto his shirt.

"Jesus H. Christ," his father said.

Cliff stopped in mid-chew and looked at his chest.

"Christ-all-goddamn-mighty," his father said. He tossed his dog at the cardboard box. It missed. "On a white goddamn shirt."

While his father ripped napkins from a dispenser, Cliff used his own napkin to wipe the splotch.

"No, goddamn it," his father shouted.

Then, out of nowhere, invisible as a bee's wing, his father's palm clapped against Cliff's cheek. Cliff's hot dog fell and his ear rang loudly, from his jaw to his scalp line. His father's hand was big, as big as Cliff's whole face. The sting of it reddened. Cliff could feel it heat up, like the hot busy legs of bees bumbling to a stop against his cheek. Several people stopped, then continued. A woman with a child shook her head. And then Cliff's eyes erupted. He started to cry and he couldn't stop it.

"Stop it," his father said.

Cliff tried to say he couldn't, but he couldn't.

"Stop it before I smack you again," his father said.

"Go ahead," Cliff shouted. "Go ahead, punch me, I don't care." The tears streamed off his cheeks, onto his shirt, onto the mustard. His father looked around.

"Please, Cliffy. Come on, stop it."

"Why do you have to be so mean?" Cliff said.

"I didn't mean to hit you so hard."

He pressed a napkin to Cliff's nose. Cliff slapped it away.

"I was just trying to wipe it," Cliff explained between sobs.

"You were making it worse," his father said.

"I don't care."

His father mouthed "He's okay" to a couple of gawkers, who nodded, grinning as if they understood. Cliff continued to cry, his head bowed, his eyes fixed on the blurry, dirty floor.

"Come on, Cliff, I'm sorry."

"No you're not."

"Hey, look," his father said, shaking him from the shoulders. "We are not gonna let this ruin the whole day, you hear me?"

"I told you I don't even want a lousy hot dog."

"Watch your tone," he said. "You just watch your tone."

Back in the men's room, the man with the thick-framed glasses bent over a sink. At a sink three down, Cliff's father rolled up his sleeves again, then edged behind Cliff.

"Remember, don't touch anything. I'll do the faucets." With his fingers covered again in towels, he turned on the cold and pushed Cliff's head toward the spigot.

Cliff looked at the man who'd looked at him. He thought now might be a good time to get the man in trouble.

"That man looked at me," he told his father.

The man straightened up and pulled down a paper towel.

"What man?" his father said.

"Him," Cliff said, jutting his jaw at the man.

The man smiled.

"Cute kid," he said. He dropped his towel in the wastebasket and walked out.

Cliff's father watched him leave.

"He just thinks you're cute," he said, squeezing Cliff's shoulder. "He don't know you're tough. Girls, crybabies, tattletales, they can be cute. Not tough guys, right?"

"Yeah," Cliff said.

"Your mother asks, we took a walk, okay?"

"Okay," Cliff muttered.

He scrubbed Cliff's cheeks and eyes vigorously.

"We'll tell your brother we went into the dugout, how's that?"

Cliff squeezed his eyes tightly against the soap.

"The Yankee dugout. He'll be jealous the whole way home."

Cliff said, "Sure."

"Won't he?"

"I have to pee again," he told his father.

"What?" his father said, catching Cliff's eye in the mirror. "After you wash up?"

Cliff nodded.

His father said, "Jesus H-," then stopped. "OK," he said, shaking his head. "Go ahead. Keep your sleeves rolled."

Alongside the ramp that led to their box seats, they stopped at a souvenir stand. Cliff's father bought two official American League baseballs that had been autographed by the whole Yankee team. Cliff was to use one as proof that they'd been inside the dugout. Then, later, on the way home, when the unfairness of Cliff getting to visit the Yankee dugout was about to make Wally cry, he could give him the other one.

But on the Grand Central Parkway, Wally insisted that the autographed baseballs were bogus. "Like Mickey Mantle's got time to sign baseballs," Wally said. He tossed the ball back onto Cliff's lap.

"Yeah?" Cliff said. "Then who signed them?"

Wally shook his head. "You are such a baby." He pressed his mitt up against the window and used it as a pillow.

"Cut it out, you two," their father said. Through the rearview mirror he pinpointed their locations.

"It's true," Wally said. "They get the hot dog guys to sign them, then babies like Quiffy cough up their milk money."

"I said that's enough."

Wally rolled his eyes, then shut them. Cliff gave him the finger on his knee. He held it there from Flushing, Queens, all the way through Smithtown, Suffolk County, where the Northern State Parkway ended. Sometimes he aimed the finger at his father, sometimes his mother, where they argued in the front seat. They argued quietly because Wally slept and because Cliff pretended to. Sometimes they smoked and stared silently, the only sound the rush of the wind through the slightly cracked windows. If Wolf was in the car, he'd have his nose pressed into the crack, vacuuming in the riot of fast new smells. Cliff's father would say be careful, and make Cliff hold onto the dog, as if Wolf could jump through a crack. Cliff pictured Wolf in the backyard now, tugging at the end of his rope, yelping and howling, as if that would bring Cliff home any sooner. Cliff loved that Wolf could yelp and howl like that and never seem ashamed after.

In Smithtown their father woke them at the statue of the bull. "There's the bull," he told them. "What do you say?"

Wally blinked, rolled his eyes, and put his head back on the baseball glove.

"What do you say?" their father repeated.

They were supposed to say "olé," but neither of them answered. Cliff wondered which one would get in trouble.

"Your father asked you something," their mother said. An instant later Cliff's finger was in Wally's fist and bent back past where the knuckle cracked. Cliff shouted.

"Hey," their father said.

Wally said, "He had a bee on him."

"Yeah, right," Cliff said.

"I think it was a yellow jacket."

"Hey, I'm warning the two of you."

When they pulled into their development, Cliff slunk down in his seat. He didn't want to see his friends, he just wanted to play with Wolf. Cliff hoped his friends were out somewhere playing baseball, a twi-night double header. He didn't want to have to explain to them how he never got his real autograph. The prospect of talking about the game fatigued him. He'd wonder if they could tell he'd been hit, or that his father had ruined the game. To them, Cliff's father was a hero, the only Marine on the block, the man with all the muscles, and all the trophies for having those muscles. To them, Cliff's father was the guy who got the box seats, right-field box seats.

They pulled into the driveway. Cliff hadn't seen anyone, but while his mother and father and Wally stepped from the car, he watched through the rear window making sure.

"You coming?" his father asked.

"In a minute."

"Come on," his father said. "We'll have a catch."

"That's OK."

"We'll have an ice cream sandwich."

"I gotta feed Wolf," Cliff said.

"He's not doing anything," his mother said, "until he changes out of those clothes."

In the backyard, Cliff rolled around on the chewed-up lawn with Wolf. They played "front-fang tug-of-war" and Cliff did all the things that made Wolf pretend he was angry. He squeezed his nose, tapped his snout, lifted him by his chest. Wolf growled louder and louder, but it was all play. Nothing made him angry, although he pretended really well.

On the side patio, along a tall row of arborvitae hedge, Wolf spotted Cliff's father. He unclamped Cliff's fingers and bounded off, leaping into Cliff's father's chest. Cliff's father caught the dog and swung him side to side. This was their game.

"Yes," he said, "he's the big bad Wolf, yes. The big bad pussycat, yes."

Wolf covered his face in licks. Cliff's father licked him back. They had a tongue fight until Cliff's father put him down.

Cliff called, "Here, Wolf," but the dog continued bouncing around Cliff's father's legs, play biting. "Butter-bites" his father called them.

"You tell him what a bastard I am?" Cliff's father asked.

"I didn't tell him anything."

His father tried to pull his fingers from Wolf's teeth. "Go ahead," he told the dog, "go play with your brother."

Wolf got his sleeve and tried pulling that.

"He don't know he's supposed to be mad at me, huh?"

"I said I didn't tell him anything."

Cliff's father pulled the dog with him and sat alongside Cliff. "OK, Wolfie," he said. "Enough." With barely an effort he flipped Wolf onto his back. Wolf held up his four paws for Cliff's father to scratch him. "Yeah, that's good access to a fat itchy belly, yeah."

He looked at Cliff. "You want to scratch him, too?"

"It's OK," Cliff said. "I scratched him this morning."

"You scratched him this morning," Cliff's father repeated, and started laughing. He laughed hard, as if he couldn't control it. "You scratched him this morning. So what, now he's done? That's all he gets?"

"No," said Cliff. "I don't know."

"You don't want to scratch him because then your hand would be near my hand?"

His father's hand roamed over Wolf's upper belly. It reminded Cliff of an old-timer's four-fingered baseball glove, thick-fingered, leathery, huge but cartoonish, scuffed at the knuckles. The fingernails were clean as glass.

"Your hand might actually touch my hand?"

Cliff didn't answer.

"Go ahead," his father said, "scratch him. I'll stop. Go ahead. You want to."

Cliff's father took his hand off Wolf's belly and let Cliff scratch the dog. Wolf pawed at Cliff's father's arms.

They sat like that for several minutes, in expectation. Cliff knew an apology was coming, and he knew he wouldn't be able to resist, and he hated himself for that weakness, and he hated his father for making him cry, and he hated feeling like he might cry now.

"You're not going to play with your friends?" his father asked.

Cliff shook his head.

"Go ahead. You can take Wolf with you. Just keep him on a leash."

"Maybe later," Cliff said.

"It's gonna be dark soon," his father said. "You won't be able to play."

"Yeah," he said, testing his father. He wanted to see how apologetic he really was—if the million idiotic rules could relax. His father bristled, but he didn't say anything. "I just feel like playing with Wolf," Cliff said.

"You don't want to have to talk about the game?"

"Not really."

"You don't want to tell them I ruined the game."

"It wasn't ruined."

"It's no fun to tell people about bad times, is it? I even ruined your birthday, didn't I?"

Cliff shrugged.

"I did a stupid thing out there today, huh?"

"I don't know."

"A mean thing, right? It was a mean thing."

"It's OK," Cliff said.

"Go ahead, you can say it."

"It's OK."

He looked at Cliff, smiled, and nodded. He extended his hand. "Friends?" he asked.

Cliff nodded.

"You're not gonna shake?"

"I can't," Cliff said. "The dog—"

"All right, so you shake one paw, I'll shake the other. That'll be like we're all shaking."

They all three shook, Wolf play-nipping at their fingers.

"Thanks for not telling your mother," Cliff's father said. "You did a good thing, she gets too upset."

"You're welcome."

Cliff knew he shouldn't be thanked. Technically, he didn't tell his mother. But she knew by everything he didn't say, and everything he did. It was a game they played in this family. Only stating things made them real. Otherwise, they hadn't happened.

Cliff's father removed one of the autographed balls from a pocket and bounced it a few times on his palm.

"It's really not the same thing, is it?"

"It's all right," Cliff said.

"Nah," his father said. "It's a piece of crap."

He tossed it for Wolf, but the dog just watched it roll indifferently, then pawed Cliff's father's near arm.

"Look, even Wolf don't want it."

"Wolf only likes snowballs, and dirt bombs."

"Don't throw dirt bombs," Cliff's father said.

"I won't," Cliff said.

His father crossed his legs at the ankles and pressed himself up with no hands. "I'll see you inside."

"OK."

"Don't come in with your shoes on."

"I won't."

"And shake out your cuffs."

"Right," Cliff said.

The following week, while mowing the back lawn, Cliff would find the autographed baseball his father had tossed. He'd pick it up, run his fingers over the dew-hardened cover, attempt to read the rain-streaked ink, the signatures now indecipherable blue spaghetti. And he'd throw it over the hedges into the Semars' yard, where early in October Kevin Semar ("you see less with Semar") would find it and claim he'd gotten it signed in the dugout.

Tonight, inside, everything would be back to normal. Cliff's father would be a great guy. They'd eat ice cream sandwiches in front of the TV. He'd crack jokes about the neighbors, their mother would disapprove, and then they'd go to bed. Later, Cliff's father's nightmares would wake the house. When the moaning subsided, and Cliff found himself too rattled to fall back to sleep, he'd get up and follow the flickering light and the whispering voices of the television into the living room where his father rocked in the rocking chair and drank cold milk from the carton. His father might pat for Cliff to get up on his lap, where Cliff would fall asleep to the military cadences his father's fingers tap-tap-tapped into his head. Or his father might point to the floor, where Cliff could sit between his ankles and try to tickle away the fire in his calloused, burning feet.

Tim Tomlinson teaches at the Writer's Voice in Manhattan.

SHAKESPEARE, DNA, AND NATURAL PROFIT / *Frederick Turner*

S INCE THE INDUSTRIAL REVOLUTION of the late eighteenth century the dominant model of industry has been one of the exploitation of natural resources. In the traditional mode of subsistence and husbandry, farmers and peasants labored like Adam in the Old Testament to make the earth fruitful. But the new class of entrepreneurs rejected this Neolithic mode of thought. The lords of the mines, cotton mills and railroads wanted a faster accumulation of capital. Enlightened capitalists like Josiah Wedgwood, the eighteenth-century pottery king and philosopher, wanted not only to make money but also to inaugurate a culture and society that would liberate the human race from drudgery and oppression. But progress depended upon the conquest of nature. Thus they accelerated economic activity by felling forests, burning fossil fuels, damming rivers, tearing up the earth for mines and construction, and finally harnessing the substance of human life by time and work studies. Instead of living inefficiently off the interest generated by natural increase, they broke into nature's capital assets and dismantled them to create an urban world.

Given the science available to the first industrialists, this model made perfect sense; no alternative would have been "realistic." The Newtonian physics bequeathed by the eighteenth century to the nineteenth had portrayed the universe as a piece of clockwork. Clockwork has two characteristics: it is predictable in its operations (the whole virtue of a clock is predictability!) and it runs down. Living things are just another part of the machine; their growth and development is merely a temporary gain made at the cost of a greater diminution in natural order elsewhere, and with the prospect of extinction when those resources give out. As part of the universe we too are subject to economic and historical determinism. If the universe is running down, then we are in competition with one another and with nature for a diminishing stockpile of usable energy.

The nineteenth-century science of thermodynamics triumphantly confirmed this analysis: disorder (entropy) increases irreversibly with time, and we are here, as Matthew Arnold put it, "upon a darkling plain/Where ignorant armies clash by night"—the light is growing dimmer and chaos mounts. Thus our only defense as human beings is to burn up the available order in the natural universe at a rate that is faster than the natural decay of the world, so as to fuel human progress and enlightenment. Civilizations decline and fall; and the social classes are locked in a relentless conflict over resources and labor. Malthus foresaw a final collapse, as the human population overwhelmed the natural resources of the planet. Wagner portrayed the final victory of the forces of darkness in the *Götterdämmerung,* and Oswald Spengler gave it historical form in *The Decline of the West.*

We in the twentieth century have largely inherited this view of the world, despite the fact that it is now, as I shall show, so incomplete as to be scientifically obsolete. Whenever we speak of dwindling natural resources, of America's disproportionate consumption of energy, of sharing out the national wealth in a fairer manner or of liberation from biological destiny, we are unconsciously adopting the rhetoric of nineteenth-century industrial exploiters and the nineteenth-century revolutionaries who sought to despoil them of their gains. But the rhetoric itself limits what we can think. A new scientific vision of the world is emerging, one which has much in common with the traditions of husbandry and natural fruitfulness that were replaced by the model of industrial exploitation, though at the same time the new vision makes possible a rate of progress undreamed of by the peasant and the farmer. The word "progress" itself needs to be redefined to include the ideas that nature itself generates value by the interplay and synergy of its elements, and that human economic activity is a continuation of the natural process of evolution and increase. As the master of the supremely synergistic art of drama, and as an inhabitant of an age in which old ideas of husbandry and new concepts of technological progress coexisted and could be compared and combined, Shakespeare is uniquely qualified to guide us in this process of redefinition. For Shakespeare the ideal form of economic work is gardening. What does gardening mean in his poetic vision, and what does it mean for economics and business, which is the primary target of this essay?

In *The Winter's Tale* there is a little episode which has profound implications. The shepherdess Perdita (who is actually a foundling foreign princess, though she does not know it) is holding a rustic feast to celebrate a successful sheep-shearing. She is in love with Florizel, prince of the realm, who is courting her in disguise, against the wishes of his father, King Polixenes. Polixenes, not wishing his son to marry a mere commoner, has disguised himself and his chief counselor Camillo in order to attend the feast and observe the prince and his beloved together, and to break up the liaison. None of the major characters in the scene are what they seem; and Shakespeare is thus inviting us to see beneath surface meanings to the inner truth. Perdita, who according to custom has been giving flowers to her guests as befits their age and station in life (spring flowers for the young, summer flowers for the mature, and so on) greets her distinguished-looking unknown guests courteously.

> Perdita: You're welcome, sir.
> Give me those flowers there, Dorcas. Reverend sirs,
> For you there's rosemary and rue; these keep
> Seeming and savor all the winter long.
> Grace and remembrance be to you both,
> And welcome to our shearing!

Like young people in any century, Perdita thinks that anyone over forty is old, and so she gives her guests flowers suitable for septuagenarians. Rather amused, Polixenes gently teases her for this.

> Polixenes: Shepherdess—
> A fair one are you—well you fit our ages
> With flowers of winter.

Perdita recovers from her embarrassment, excusing herself on the grounds that she doesn't have appropriate late-summer flowers to give them:

> Perdita: Sir, the year growing ancient,
> Not yet on summer's death, nor on the birth
> Of trembling winter, the fairest flowers o' th' season
> Are our carnations and streaked gillyvors,
> Which some call Nature's bastards; of that kind
> Our rustic garden's barren; and I care not
> To get slips of them.

She refuses to grow the gaudier summer flowers, hinting that there is something improper in their ancestry. A "slip" is a cutting, from which a new plant can be propagated or cloned. Polixenes pursues the matter, intrigued by Perdita's evident discernment, eloquence and strength of mind.

> Polixenes: Wherefore, gentle maiden,
> Do you neglect them?

Perdita: For I have heard it said,
There is an art, which in their piedness shares
With great creating Nature.

But now she has raised one of the perennial questions of philosophy. What she has just said is that she objects to the art of selective breeding and hybridization by which Renaissance horticulturists transformed simple wildflowers into elaborate multicolored blooms. Like an ardent advocate of environmental purity in our own time, she is suspicious of artificial interventions into nature. There is perhaps a further unconscious thought lurking in her mind. She has just been anxiously worrying about her own presumption in entertaining the amorous advances of a prince, whose blood and breeding are far above what she imagines to be her own humble origins. Nature and human art should not mix, nor should commoners and nobility; if they do, appearances become deceptive. Perdita is innocent, straightforward and honest and dislikes adulteration and deceit. Her decision not to cultivate the carnations and gillyvors is based on a personal code of sincerity:

Perdita: I'll not put
The dibble in earth, to set one slip of them;
No more than were I painted, I would wish
This youth to say 'twere well, and only therefore
Desire to breed by me.

Perdita dislikes the hybrid flowers because they use their attractive looks to gain the advantage of being reproduced instead of their more modest sisters. It is as if she were to paint herself with cosmetics in order to make Florizel cultivate her with *his* "dibble" (garden trowel). The "art" that Perdita eschews had a wide range of meaning. It could mean art in the contemporary sense of what we find in an art gallery, a book of poetry, a symphony hall or a theater. But it was a normal term, too, for skill or technique, and by extension for technology, machinery and mechanical devices of all kinds. It also meant magic, alchemy and the mystical sciences of astrology and prognostication. Finally, it could mean deceptive practice or cunning imposture.

The ambivalence and complexity implicit in Perdita's use of the term are quite familiar in our own times. At present we are struggling with the ethical and health implications of the science of genetic engineering by means of recombinant DNA. Should we buy the new genetically altered tomatoes on the grocery shelves, or drink the milk produced with the aid of bovine hormones? What about the strawberries with their chimeric pesticide genes, or the experimental fruitflies with eyes growing out of their legs and antennae, the patented strains of cancerous mice? Reading Shakespeare we become aware that our problems are not new; Perdita's unease prefigures ours. Indeed, since the Neolithic agricultural revolution, when we first began selecting plants and animals to breed future stock, we have been in the business of genetic engineering and recombinant DNA. Our humblest domestic and culinary techniques are just as "unnatural" as the activities of the biochemists. Brewer's yeast, sourdough, ginger ale plants and cheese-mites are all examples of human tinkering with natural genetic processes. When we divide a clump of irises in the garden we are literally practicing clone technology; when we enter a pedigreed dog or cat or pigeon in a show we are practicing eugenics on an entire species. When we choose what we believe to be an exceptionally kind, intelligent, attractive, healthy and honest person to be our mate and bear or sire our children, we are engaged in human eugenics on our own local scale. There is no escape.

Thus Perdita cannot evade the fact that as a tool-using animal—the "dibble" with which she gardens is a cunning little technological device—she must alter nature in order to survive. She needs "art" in its technological sense. Likewise, as a social, role-performing animal she must put on appearances—her festive party dress—in order to coexist with other humans (the theatrical sense of "art"). Yet she has a point. It is only nature that is creative, that has the power to grow and reproduce; and it is only when one deals with the inner person rather than the outer social mask that one can obtain true commitment and sincerity from someone. But when she disparages the gillyvors because of the art that went into their ancestry, Polixenes replies:

> Say there be;
> Yet Nature is made better by no mean
> But Nature makes that mean; so over that art
> Which you say adds to Nature, is an art
> That Nature makes. You see, sweet maid, we marry
> A gentler scion to the wildest stock,
> And make conceive a bark of baser kind
> By bud of nobler race. This is an art
> Which does mend Nature, change it rather; but
> The art itself is Nature.

The image that Polixenes uses to explain the relationship between nature and art is the horticultural technology of grafting. This is what he means when he speaks of marrying a "gentler scion to the wildest stock." A gardener or vineyard-tender will cut off the upper stem of a vigorous wild plant and bind to the stock that remains the stem and upper branches of a more delicate hybrid. Nature is accommodating enough to allow the graft to "take," and the two plants are fused into one. The resulting combination has the virtues of both—the resistance to disease, pests, and frost of the wild stock and the hybrid's desired characteristics of productiveness, excellence of fruit or flower, or perfume.

The main point of Polixenes' remarks is that the art of genetic engineering by which we alter nature was itself created by nature. The plain ancestral gillyvors have the genetic potential to produce the gaudy streaks that attract the eye and persuade human gardeners to propagate them. Humans become a way for streaked gillyvors to make more streaked gillyvors, to extend the diversity of the gillyvor species by branching out a new breed specially adapted to the environment of human culture. The gillyvor is by nature an art-using plant. And we humans are by nature art-using animals. We survived to reproduce because we had the capacity to make tools like sheephooks or dibbles and breed domestic species like sheep or gillyvors for our own purposes. Moreover, our capacity to make fictions—to tell lies and put on disguises and mount plays and enhance our looks by clothing or cosmetics—is likewise a natural one, like the eagle's to fly or the mole's to dig. It is of a piece with our ability to express our thoughts in words, and to build families, tribes, cities and nations.

Human art, human fiction, human invention, human technology are not unnatural forces that have suddenly supervened upon nature; they are the continuation of nature's own mysterious capacity to grow and reproduce. Furthermore, human economic production cannot be separated from human reproduction; the family is still the primary unit of economic cooperation, and marriage is the major means of distributing the wealth that accrues to production. It is against Polixenes' wishes that Florizel intends to marry a wild shepherdess, but by using metaphors of social class to describe the graft—"gentler," "baser," "nobler"—Polixenes has shown the fallacy of his own objections.

His immediate purpose is to show Perdita that her hard-and-fast distinction between sterile insincere art and creative honest nature will not hold up. Nature will accept the graft of the wild and the artificial: nature can be artistic, art can be natural. Art and appearances can possess the same sincerity, faithfulness and inner trustworthiness that Florizel compares to the seeds of the earth. This does not mean, of course, that untruths and disguises are always harmless. To the contrary. After all Polixenes has disguised himself with the evil intent of preventing his son's marriage. Though he will later repent of his anger when he finds out that Perdita is exactly the kind of grafted hybrid he has described—a princess by birth, cut off from her ancestral roots and grafted onto the stock of a peasant family—in the meantime his lies and deception are quite as dangerous and harmful as they are anywhere else in Shakespeare's plays. Nevertheless, it is by means of disguises and subterfuges also that Florizel and Perdita escape the wrath of the king. There is nothing wrong in themselves with fictions, contrivances and masks, nor are such things unique to human society: the gillyvors mask themselves in order to be cultivated.

So the issue has changed profoundly. It is no longer a matter of having to choose between the innocent creative sincerity of nature and the sophisticated sterile deceptions of art, a choice in which we would be forced to abandon all the advantages of technology, consciousness, language and social communication if we were to opt for moral purity. Art and nature are one: we must now use our judgment—not some simple formula that labels one "impure" and the other "pure"—to choose between courses of action.

Such decisions do not extend only to matters of horticulture and other technologies, nor even to our social and economic arrangements, as the whole sexual subtext of this wonderfully subtle passage of Shakespeare implies. Even in matters of human reproduction there is no comfortable dividing line between art and nature. The very choice of marriage partner is itself a reproductive technology, favoring one set of human characteristics over another in the propagation of the species. If in the future we develop biotechnological means for healing or improving the genome of the human embryo, this capability will be new only in its scope and speed, not in its essentially difficult and problematic character. After all, a woman who chooses for the father of her children a good, honest and intelligent man is discriminating against some other potential mate whom she has consciously or unconsciously judged less worthy of continuing the species. But this also means that we should not be squeamish in continuing to improve our control over our own genetic future. The damage, so to speak, has already been done; even before human beings came along, nature, like the gillyvors that use their colors to attract bees that will help them reproduce, had already been taking control of its own evolution.

Nature is the realm of growth; but as Shakespeare was well aware, it is also the realm of decay. The nineteenth-century thermodynamic view of the world as irreversibly running down is still true as far as it goes. Indeed, this idea is the central problem that Shakespeare addresses in the Sonnets. Time in the Sonnets is a devourer, a thief, a merciless legal prosecutor, a relentless creditor who demands full payment of the debt of life, with interest. Living organisms can grow and reproduce but the more advanced, beautiful and individuated they are, the more fragile, and the more definitively they die:

> Since brass, nor stone, nor earth, nor boundless sea,
> But sad mortality o'ersways their power,
> How with this rage shall beauty hold a plea,
> Whose action is no stronger than a flower?

Shakespeare's answers to this question anticipate the new science of the late twentieth century. The issue for him is posed in the most personal terms: how can the beloved be protected from aging, death and corruption? His first answer is that his dear young friend must marry, and beget a child who will preserve his beauty.

> Then being asked where all thy beauty lies...
> How much more praise deserved thy beauty's use,
> If thou could'st answer, "This fair child of mine
> Shall sum my count, and make my old excuse..."

In several sonnets the idea of sexual reproduction as a defense against time is imaged in frankly economic terms, as an investment that earns compound interest. The sum that we invest was itself loaned to us by nature; we do wrong if we spend it on ourselves, or even invest it in ourselves at high rates of interest, for if we do it will perish with us.

> Profitless usurer, why doest thou use
> So great a sum of sums yet cannot live?
> For having traffic with thyself alone,
> Thou of thyself thy sweet self doth deceive.
> Then how when Nature calls thee to be gone,
> What acceptable audit canst thou leave?
> Thy unused beauty must be tombed with thee,

Which, used, lives th'executor to be.

When the original business of loan of life must be repaid, the profits made by using the money—one's children—remain. This is a tough-minded equation of personal and financial values, but it has a strange ring of truth. In another sonnet it is quite clear that Shakespeare, who observed the methods of livestock breeders just as Charles Darwin did over two hundred years later, has already grasped the principle of evolution through natural selection:

> Let those whom Nature hath not made for store,
> Harsh, featureless, and rude, barrenly perish.
> Look whom she best endowed, she gave the more;
> Which bounteous gift thou shouldst in bounty cherish.
> She carved thee for her seal, and meant thereby
> Thou shouldst print more, not let that copy die.

This first answer to the problem of time and decay is exactly that of life itself, as described by evolutionary biology. "Those whom Nature hath not made for store," that is, the graceless, primitive and unfit, must not survive to reproduce; those whose subtle complexity is evidenced by their beauty should print themselves genetically into the future. Living organisms preserve their inner genetic structures, and thus conquer death and decay, by reproducing themselves into another generation.

But such an answer is as unsatisfactory to Shakespeare as it is to us. Certainly the general type is preserved by reproduction. Asexually reproducing organisms can make exact copies of themselves. But it is precisely the individuality of a loved human being that we miss when it is gone; and that individuality is the product of sexual reproduction, which creates a unique recombination of genes for each new birth. In other words, the process of sexual reproduction that Shakespeare recommends to preserve his friend's beauty is the guarantee that his individuality, the essence of his beauty, is biologically irreproducible. Shakespeare's second answer to the problem of time, the preservative agency of poetry, is proposed at first as an inadequate stopgap measure; parenthood is still "a mightier way" to "make war upon this bloody tyrant Time." But as he examines it, it makes more and more sense.

Shakespeare sets out to eternalize his friend's beauty in the very art by which he mourns its passing:

> But thy eternal summer shall not fade,
> Nor lose possession of that fair thou ow'st,

Nor shall Death brag thou wand'rest in his shade
When in eternal lines to time thou grow'st.
So long as men can breathe and eyes can see,
So long lives this, and this gives life to thee.

We today are reading those lines, so the solution has worked for four hundred years at least. What is especially significant is that poetry is being described as a higher form of sexual reproduction. Both are what Shakespeare calls "lines of life, that life repair." These lines of life are the lineage of a family that replaces the dying with the newborn, but they are also the lines of poetry. It is as if he has guessed that the genetic code that specifies the shape of our bodies is a line or thread, like the long thread of letters that make up a poem. DNA is indeed a thread of nucleotides, which spell out the "words" and "sentences" of the genes, which in turn determine the proteins that make up the human body. The words in which this beautiful relationship is being conducted find for themselves a form of repeated rhymes and metrical rhythms that are able to reprint themselves in memory and books, as DNA does, by peeling its double helix apart and printing the sequence of nucleotides anew upon the raw material within the cell. But poetry is a higher form of reproduction, for it can capture and preserve the mind and individuality of an organism, not just its bodily composition. Living reproduction can outwear the enduring metals and stone with which we build monuments to defy the effects of time. But poetry, which is spiritual, intangible and apparently fragile, is more enduring still:

Not marble, nor the gilded monuments
Of princes, shall outlive this powerful rhyme,
But you shall shine more bright in these contents
Than unswept stone, besmeared with sluttish time.

What Shakespeare now does is *graft* the new, cultural form of reproduction upon the old, biological form:

And, all in war with Time for love of you,
As he takes from you, I engraft you new.

Poetry is to living reproduction what living reproduction is to the enduring hardness of the stone and metal out of which we build monuments to defy time's decay. Poetry is grafted onto natural inheritance, so that both the generic and unconscious elements of what we wish to preserve, and also the individual and self-aware elements, are protected.

Shakespeare's vision of an economics of natural fecundity can help us move from the thermodynamic pessimism of the Industrial Revolution to a new vision of life-affirming economic progress. The confusion of poetic or living order with thermodynamic order is perhaps the biggest intellectual mistake of Modernism. The nineteenth-century notion of the world as containing a diminishing stockpile of natural value is rapidly becoming obsolete. Certainly, in thermodynamic fashion, stone and metal wear out in time. The "hungry ocean" gains "advantage in the kingdom of the shore," but then the "firm soil," in the form of encroaching sand dunes or salt marshes, takes over what was once the ocean's. It is a zero-sum game; one realm's gain is another's loss, and meanwhile chaos itself increases a little at the expense of both—"state itself confounded to decay." But in a living ecosystem, on the other hand, one species' gain is not necessarily another species' loss. The story of biological evolution is largely one of cooperation, synergy, symbiosis. Competition, even natural violence, can be just a fiercer form of cooperation. As the Eskimos say, the wolf protects the herd: prey species such as caribou rely upon their predators to cull out unfit individuals and preserve the genetic vigor of the survivors. What is waste for one species is food and fuel for another; what is death for one species (such as Douglas firs) is the womb and cradle of others (funguses and beetles).

There is no reason why human ingenuity and manufacturing should not fit itself comfortably into the creative increase of life. Living things grow in a rhythm limited only by their previous increment of growth—that is, in one cycle of growth they can add to their size by a proportion somewhere between none at all and doubling their previous size. The best sustainable rate of growth seems to be at a ratio of about 61.8 percent in each cycle. This ratio is known as the "golden ratio," and is obtained very simply by creating a series of numbers known as the Fibonnaci series, each number of which is the sum of the previous two, and then working out how fast they increase. For example, if we begin with 1, the next number in the series must also be 1— that is, 1 plus zero (there was no previous term in the series). The next number is 2 (1 + 1). The next is 3 (2 + 1), the next 5 (3 + 2), the next 8, the next 13, the next 21, and so on. If we divide 21 into 13 to obtain the percentage of increase, we get .618 or 61.8 percent, and the percentage gets more and more exact as the numbers increase. Leonardo Fibonnaci, the discoverer of this series, obtained it by trying to figure out how many rabbits he would get from a single breeding pair after a given number of generations. This growth rhythm expresses itself elegantly in the spirals of seashells and sunflower heads, in the fronds of ferns, the branchings of trees, and throughout the realms of life. Sixty-one and eight-tenths percent is nature's own profit margin, and this is surely enough for the most enthusiastic business entrepreneur. The trick is to get in synch with nature's own highly efficient processes while still fulfilling one's human goals. The art of doing this is called gardening or husbandry. We need a gardening economics.

But even before life emerged, the universe was already capable of spontaneously generating new forms of organization. Before life, new kinds of crystals, polymers and other complex molecular structures were already precipitating out of the universe as it expanded and cooled. New atomic nuclei were condensing in the hot wombs of young stars. Each new creation carries its own requirements for existence, even its own primitive and emergent values. And this enormous natural increase—what we might call natural profit—is achieved without violating any of the gloomy laws of thermodynamics that so depressed our ancestors in the nineteenth century. Usable energy is still running out and thermodynamic disorder is still increasing with time. However, the chemist Ilya Prigogine has shown that in open systems far-from-equilibrium states can arise by chance, and these far-from-equilibrium states can in turn give spontaneous birth to new forms of organization that solve the problems presented by the disequilibrium. Living organisms are the classic examples of such forms. Using this phenomenon of self-organization, what Prigogine calls the "dissipative systems" of chemistry and life—and human culture—manage to finesse the process of decay, turning the increase of disorder into the increase of information. They then need only trivial amounts of energy to order that information in more and more elegant ways. Thus there is a net increase in usable knowledge that outpaces the growth of physical disorder.

Here again a kind of "gardening economics" suggests itself. Industry need no longer "burn" huge amounts of natural order to force its will upon matter and turn out mass-produced product. Instead, it might discover the far-from-equilibrium situations that crop up throughout nature, finding ways to tweak existing natural processes so as to bring about economically desirable results. In fact industry has already begun doing this on a large scale, as the expansion of the biotechnological sector of contemporary business demonstrates. Tinkering with a few genes in a test tube, we create immunities that save thousands of bushels of crops from pests and diseases. Industry is also making extensive use of catalytic chemistry, chaotic mixing processes and the like—those processes in the inorganic world that anticipate the ingenious economy of life. Just as microscopic chips of silicon can now efficiently control the roar of a mighty dump-truck engine, so we can use the efficient leverages offered to us by nature itself to harness the grand natural forces of our living universe. Industrial chemistry loves to exploit those states of matter at the boundaries between the solid, liquid, gaseous and plasma states, or between different crystalline or chemical configurations, where, far from equilibrium, only a small change of temperature, light, chemistry or pressure can produce large results: including metals with useful properties, self-adjusting sunglasses, liquid crystal displays, efficient fuel injection or highly sensitive measuring devices such as the home pregnancy test. It took a huge expense of coal and oil and iron ore to develop the cybernetic control systems that now require only a few ounces of silicon and a tiny flow of current to maintain, and which are in turn radically diminishing our need for fossil fuels and ores.

Shakespeare's reasoning endorses the control and readaptation of natural processes for human purposes. Bio-engineering, even including the altering of human genes, is ethically defensible, since nature has already been engaged in the activity for billions of years, and the ability to perform it ourselves was given to us by nature. In Spielberg's and Crichton's Jurassic Park, and in a great many other politically correct popular entertainments, there is an implicit argument that God made living organisms and that they should not be tampered with or claimed as intellectual property. This idea leads immediately to absurdities. It would, for instance, make it illegal to sell thoroughbred horses and cattle or put them out to stud, to market meats and vegetables in a grocery store (all normal grocery foods are the result of genetic alteration by selective breeding of plants or animals), or even to charge students for tuition (the "product" of a school or university is the knowledge embedded in the students' brain cells). Carried to its furthest extreme, such logic would even forbid marriage, since marriage connects economic obligations with selective reproductive planning.

This is not to say that *any* proposed genetic intervention is permissible. Genetics is a fantastically complex subject, and it is extremely difficult to predict the consequences of actions in this area. The ethics governing any weighty, far-reaching decision apply more strongly to biogenetic intervention than anywhere else. The work should be fail-safe, and every possible consequence should be examined. But on the other hand, all human decisions are subject to unpredictable consequences; this is the potential tragedy of action. The deep footprint I leave running across the wet field nearby may trip a child and break her neck. Every time a couple get married and start a family, they are taking enormous risks. Would the parents of Adolf Hitler have had children if they had foreseen the result? Can one imagine any worse catastrophe than the birth of this man, generated by routine gene recombination in sexual reproduction? The risks of gene technology, licensed and regulated by patent, look small by comparison.

Economic enterprise can imitate the natural productiveness of living and other nonlinear dynamic systems. But there is a further implication in the passages from the Sonnets and *The Winter's Tale* cited here, that suggests there is a productiveness in art and poetry which, when grafted onto life, can outdo the productivity of life itself. If industry models itself upon thermodynamics it will extract smaller and smaller amounts of value from a dying world. If it models itself upon life, it will create a sustainable economy. But if it grafts onto the life-model the additional model of art and poetry, it will begin to achieve miracles.

Shakespeare's philosophy of natural and human productivity thus has further contemporary relevance, concerning the nature of advertising. Both in the Sonnets and *The Winter's Tale* he shows that the ideas and appearances of art are not necessarily deceptions, but can be new truths in themselves or revelations of old ones. Perdita's rejection of the gillyvors is based partly on her sense that they advertise—they sell the sizzle rather than the steak. Many today likewise decry advertising as the creation of artificial desires. Marxists talk of "commodity fetishism" and condemn the consumerism that they see as the result. But again, Shakespeare shows us that the art and poetry that recommend something to us and mediate our relationship to it—its advertisements—are not essentially different from the inner structures of information that shape and order the thing itself. And they are no less legitimate. DNA is a kind of poetry that organizes insensitive matter into appetite, passion, desire. The inorganic world would consider the motivations of living organisms to be artificial, inauthentic, fetishistic. Life is matter that advertises, that sells the sizzle, that disguises itself in elegant genetic and bodily structures in order to survive. Again, this is not to say that all life, all art, all advertising are beneficial and should be encouraged. Cancers are alive; and art and advertising can tell lies. By their fruits ye shall judge them, said Jesus; we must discriminate between the good and the bad in the area of genetic, poetic or corporate fictions as in any other area. There is a deeper truth in good and valid fictions that overwhelms their literal inaccuracy, and it is this by which we judge them. The deeper truth has two aspects: it honestly portrays the nature of the evolutionary process that generated the fiction in the first place; and it permits the richest possible interplay of free beings in the future.

Frederick Turner is a poet, essayist, translator, and cultural critic whose most recent books are *April Wind, Foamy Sky: The Major Poems of Miklos Radnoti* and *The Culture of Hope*.

Reviews

Rocket City
by Cathryn Alpert
MacMurray & Beck, 1995, 347 pp.,
$22.95

Comedy abounds in *Rocket City*,
Cathryn Alpert's darkly funny first
novel. In this relentlessly contemporary tale, nobody seems to have
any historical memory prior to June
16, 1945, the date of the first atomic
explosion near Alamogordo, New
Mexico—"Rocket City." But scratch
the surface and you find a comic
structure rooted in myth and fable.
The two main characters, Figman and Marilee Levitay, are self-
exiled Californians whose separate
but parallel journeys through the
New Mexico landscape lead to
involvements with unlikely bedfel-
lows. Marilee, an art therapist from
Sherman Oaks, experiences aimless
discontent for all the "merry levi-
ty" of her name, and Figman, a
former insurance adjuster in Acci-
dental Death and Dismemberment
suffers from hypochondriac "fig-
ments" of the imagination. Their
masterfully orchestrated parallel stories converge obviously only twice—
once in a narrowly avoided head-on
collision, and once again in a bar.
But they have in common frequent
migraines, a tropism for order in
a messy world, a search for fulfill-
ment and a series of coincidental
experiences.

A pattern emerges, in which the
two main characters grapple with
evil and suffering at the same time
that they are barreling headlong into
romance. Figman holes up in Arte-
sia, New Mexico, dodging a threatened lawsuit after surviving a hor-
rific auto accident. In between his
absurd attempts to find consolation
and fame as a painter, he embarks
on an ill-fated love affair before
discovering, almost by accident, a
more consummate love. Meanwhile,
Marilee, en route to Alamogordo
to marry her dull fiancé, Larry,
picks up a hitchiking dwarf, Enoch
Swann, and ends up tooling around
in the desert with him. Against her
better judgment, she is enchanted:
"He could have been a character
right out of one of her forgotten
dreams."
The novel's surprising climax
takes place in a bar called the Launch
Pad, where Marilee impulsively per-
forms an act that shows her what
it means to cause suffering. From
migraine to nuclear apocalypse, disaster looms on the horizon. Life
therefore requires of us a certain
degree of compassion. It is a familiar
theme, but Alpert's comic invention
makes it seem refreshingly new.

Heading West
by Doris Betts
Scribner, 1995, 368 pp., $12 (pb.
reissue)

Betts' novel offers an entertaining, thought-provoking and suspenseful escape into the what-ifs of our daydreams. At the center is Nancy Finch, a thirtyish, southern small-town librarian, chafing against the demands of an ailing family and the disappointments of liaisons with men who are either married or, as one character tells her, "in bad taste." While vacationing with her sister and brother-in-law, Nancy is kidnapped at gunpoint by a young, reasonably attractive man, and transported westward across the country.

A dreamer and a romantic, Nancy is at first actually caught up in the thrill of the adventure. She and her kidnapper develop an uneasy alliance, and after a few attempts at escape Nancy begins to question her tacit compliance, her need to escape her lonely, smothered life.

In evocative language, using wry and precise details, Betts illuminates Nancy's predicament. Nancy is an appealing character, armed as she is with a sharp, intelligent wit, living out the ironies of her kidnapping. A suspenseful confrontation between protagonist and antagonist in the Grand Canyon establishes Betts' abilities to create both a fascinating character study and a thriller, with vivid descriptions of the pair in their climactic moment of conflict—a moment that reverberates in unexpected ways throughout the rest of the book.

Like a satisfying daydream, the book ends with Nancy emerging from her adventure in a somewhat unrealistic and romantic fashion. Even so, the story of Nancy's circuitous release from captivity is well worth the very enjoyable time spent reading it.

Wonder Boys
by Michael Chabon
Villard Books, 1995, 368 pp., $23

Too often novels about writers troll the outworn refrain that the lifestyle is sad and lonely, the creation of art as painful as giving birth. Yet Michael Chabon's rendition of the writer's blues in his second novel, *Wonder Boys*, is so intricately orchestrated that the reader hardly recognizes the popular melody.

Failing "wonder boy" Grady Trip is cynical yet soft hearted. His sarcasm is a function of his weaknesses: his third marriage is crumbling under the weight of his extra-marital affairs, his twenty-six-hundred-page novel *Wonder Boys* is far from completion after seven years of intermittent work, and his teaching career at a small Pennsylvania college is dulled by overindulgence in alcohol and marijuana. Adding to the chaos of his life is the college's annual writing conference. With writers and editors under one roof, disaster is imminent. Who will be the next "wonder boy" is the question on everyone's lips. Grady soon finds himself on the lam from this conference with his lover's dead dog in his trunk, Marilyn Monroe's priceless satin jacket stashed in a promising student's backpack, a "fragrant ounce of Humboldt County, California" in his glove box and with his skeptical editor (but longtime friend), Terry Crabtree, riding shotgun.

The author tips his hat to another lover of the picaresque genre, Jack Kerouac, and his "free-form Arthurian hobo jazz" that influences Chabon's own prose. Chabon's writing is poetic, worldly and wise. The novel proves that an old, familiar song is still worth singing.

Firebrand: The Life of Horace Liveright
by **Tom Dardis**
Random House, 394 pp., 1995, $27.50

In post-World-War-I America, the environment surrounding the publishers Boni and Liveright was a Jazz Age in miniature, with extremes of decadence, creativity and hysteria. This entertaining, well-written biography is as much about that milieu as about the genius behind it.

Many authors and agents didn't like Jews such as Horace Liveright and Alfred A. Knopf breaking into the old WASP nest of American publishing. (Ezra Pound was only one of many anti-semites in his day, one in fact who came to his prejudice relatively late.) The suspicious, grim Theodore Dreiser—Liveright's star author—as well as T.S. Eliot, wrote letters expressing distrust of their "Jew publisher."

The beginnings of the Modern Library, Boni and Liveright's flagship imprint, can be traced back before the B & L partnership. The Boni brothers, Albert and Charles, were young New Yorkers, like Liveright, scrambling to make a living in various investment and sales schemes. Borrowing an idea from an English tobacco company that distributed miniature copies of Shakespeare's plays with bags of tobacco, they approached Whitman Chocolate Company about the possibility of offering Lilliputian books as sales perquisites. To their amazement, they got an immediate order for fifteen thousand copies. Thus they became publishers, calling the tiny books that they were soon churning out the "Little Leather Library." It was the precursor of the Modern Library, which made its debut at B & L in 1917 with twelve mostly European authors. By the 1930s the Modern Library had become an American institution, capable of boosting the flagging reputation of a writer like F. Scott Fitzgerald by merely including one of his books in the line. By then Liveright, in desperate financial straits, had sold the Modern Library to one of his previous vice-presidents, Bennett Cerf, who used it as the cornerstone to found another new publishing company, Random House.

Liveright was never satisfied to bank the profits from his publishing successes. He was perpetually overextended. Always there was a new stock to lose his money on, a new author, a new play to produce. (The American stage version of *Dracula*, with Bela Lugosi, was one of his few theatrical successes.) Among authors and would-be's, he was known as something of a pushover, ready to offer two hundred dollars and a contract to anybody with a creditable proposal. He went to great expense to woo and hold authors admired by tastemakers like H.L. Mencken and Ezra Pound (whom he paid as a "finder"), and to publish writers like Robinson Jeffers, whose poetry he personally loved despite the fact that it didn't sell.

Being a rake and an alcoholic certainly didn't help Liveright's image. Like F. Scott Fitzgerald he had a hypersensitivity to alcohol but couldn't give up the stuff. Like Fitzgerald, too, he paid for his excess in a slow but steady decline. In the house that published Dreiser, Hemingway, Faulkner, Hart Crane, e.e. cummings, Sherwood Anderson, Jean Toomer, and Djuna Barnes, the whiskey ran freely, the smoke and cynicism were thick, "girls" for visiting men authors were brought in for entertainment.

Women who worked at Liveright had to run up and down the stairs like fugitives to avoid being pinched and poked. Broadway show people flowed in and out at all times of the day.

Reading about the twenties at Boni and Liveright has the bonus effect of almost making one appreciate the much-maligned present era of political correctness.

The Liberty Campaign
by Jonathan Dee
Washington Square Press, 1995, 272 pp., $10 (pb. reissue)

In this unpretentious yet powerful second novel from Jonathan Dee, sixty-four-year-old Gene Trowbridge finds himself nearing the end of his career as a successful advertising executive. In the last days before his retirement, he finds himself deep in inevitable soul-searching when he learns that his neighbor of seven years, Albert Ferdinand, is accused of horrible crimes against humanity. Confronted with the knowledge that his own neighbor could be responsible for the torture and murder of hundreds of innocent people, Gene is forced into profound self-examination. How could he, with all the wisdom of sixty-four years, not know the worst kind of criminal from a normal man?

Fascinated with Albert's case, Gene enters into a friendly relationship with his unnervingly polite neighbor in order to discover whether Albert is actually the monster he is said to be. The two become close friends, but when Gene learns the truth he is plunged into a moral dilemma that threatens both his self-image and his image of the world. As Gene becomes more deeply involved with Albert, and the authorities close in, he is forced

to question his concept of guilt and the judgment of it.

As readable as it is important, *The Liberty Campaign* is a moral novel that parallels one man's search for truth with another man's search for repentance.

Independence Day
by Richard Ford
Knopf, 1995, 451 pp., $24

Independence Day continues the story of Frank Bascombe, narrator of Ford's acclaimed 1986 novel, *The Sportswriter*. In that book, Frank Bascombe continually told us how kind he was, how well-meaning, how lonely. But at points he seemed breathtakingly cold. Unable to understand why his wife wouldn't take him back (though he consoled himself over the death of their son by having approximately eighteen affairs), he was utterly unwilling to get close to anyone who was interested in being close to him.

At the beginning of this sequel, five years have passed. Frank now works in real estate, selling houses and managing a few properties of his own. His ex-wife has remarried and taken their children to an estate in Connecticut. While Frank misses his children (and is losing sleep over his son Paul, a barking kleptomaniac), he has achieved a certain happiness by embracing the disengagement he fought in *The Sportswriter*. Frank calls his temporary peace with the drifting life his "existence period."

This is the story of Frank reconnecting to the world, overcoming the apathy of the existence period. He has, for instance, carefully planned a trip with Paul to two sports halls of fame over the Fourth of July weekend. This despite the fact that Paul has zero interest in sports. Frank envisions having a long fatherly talk with Paul about becoming a man, so he sends his son some Emerson and a copy of the *Declaration of Independence* as background reading for their trip. Paul doesn't read a word of it, and Frank doesn't really mind. Surprisingly, the trip does make a difference in Frank's relationship with Paul, though not because they engage in lively exegesis of Emerson.

Though occasionally burdened by what Elmore Leonard has called "the parts people skip," *Independence Day* is a rollicking, colloquial, funny book. If Bascombe has matured since *The Sportswriter*, Richard Ford, with the bleak and moving story collection *Rock Springs* and the novel *Wildlife* under his belt, has become a better, more relaxed writer. This is his best book yet.

Somebody Else's Mama
by David Haynes
Milkweed, 1995, 341 pp., $21.95

Haynes' second novel chronicles the struggle of one Missouri family to achieve solidarity in the face of their disagreements. As the story begins, Paula Johnson is attempting to raise her twin sons and help with her husband's mayoral campaign. Al's political ambitions mystify Paula at the beginning of the race, but as time goes on she simply becomes angry with her husband's new views and goals. To compound Paula's problems, her mother-in-law, Miss Xenobia Kezee, has just been forcibly brought to live with the family while she recuperates from a debilitating illness. Belligerent and sometimes violent, Miss Kezee doesn't appreciate the move back to her former home, and wants to return to

Minneapolis. Al doesn't understand his mother's resentment, any more than he understands why after his father's death she fled their hometown of River Ridge—and himself.

The contest for mayor of the black community of River Ridge provides a backdrop for the story of the Johnson family. Al's push for consolidation with two other communities is supported by those who want to modernize the town, but it upsets his mother, who thinks Al should leave well enough alone. The election also causes friction between Al and Paula, who is left out of most of the decisions regarding the race.

Alienated from Al and plagued by guilt over her own mother's solitary death in a nursing home, Paula tries to heal her mother-in-law with kindness and understanding. The two form a bond, even as they are both growing farther apart from Al. Meanwhile, Al is simply trying to do what he thinks is best for the community and his family, though sometimes his priorities don't reflect this.

Haynes' skillful use of shifting viewpoints reveals the amusing disparities between what each of the characters sees as truth. *Somebody Else's Mama* is a vibrant, entertaining, thoughtful novel about the trials and tribulations of being a family.

The Only World
by Lynda Hull
HarperPerennial, 1995, 80 pp., $12

Lynda Hull's third volume of poetry, a posthumous collection of remembrances edited by her husband David Wojahn is not so much an accumulation of nostalgic experiences as a record of all that threatens to consume us. *The Only World* catalogues the deconstruction of the tangible world, past and present, into a maze of darkly romantic signifiers and reminds us of the more painful side of the past.

In "Ornithology," as in most of the poems in this collection, real-world objects and memories become fluid and dreamlike: "Macaws/scarlet and violet,/tangerine as a song/the hue of sunset where my street becomes water/and down shore this phantom city skyline's/mere hazy silhouette."

Hull insists on the necessity of memory. Nostalgia for the innocence of the past is as vital to her as the painful recollections of violence—be it the rape of a metropolis, of an entire race, or of a single resilient woman. The urban landscape becomes a touchstone for Lynda Hull's connnection to more innocent times: "The city's become a figure for the way you've learned to love/what's distant, fantastic,/an abyss of space between."

Daughters of Song
by Paula Huston
Random House, 1995, 363 pp., $23

Paula Huston's promising first novel is written with the same lyrical immediacy that has gained recognition in her short stories. Huston writes, "Deep in the heart of the city someone is practicing Beethoven." That someone is Silvia, a young pianist contending with the choices and sacrifices involved in becoming a mature artist.

With her floating curls and her innocence, combined with a passion for the piano and gritty willingness to plunge into her studies, Silvia alternates between seeming like an ethereal child and a substantial young woman. Her struggle to master Beethoven's mighty Opus

111 mirrors her inability to develop the "hard cold intellect" demanded by her instructor, the imposing Toft, and her reluctance to give up the innocence that distances her from extremes in life.

When she and her roommate are mugged, Silvia begins to examine the precarious nature of her supposedly "safe" haven of innocence. Her life becomes further complicated by the awakening of sexual passion, spurred by the attentions of an awkward, sensitive male pianist named Jan, and those of the more dynamic and sensual David. Soon Silvia faces some hard decisions about her responsibilities: to the adoring Jan, to her perfectionist father, to her disapproving instructor, to her music and most importantly, to herself.

Daughters of Song features a large cast of characters, and Huston gives more than passing notice to the homeless people whom Silvia and the other musicians pass on their way to the conservatory. Music, like the ripples from an object thrown into water, touches the many characters and binds them loosely but irrefutably.

Huston's novel is a story of the anticipatory excitement and timorous dread of growing up, of making choices and recognizing sacrifices.

Alexandra
by Valerie Martin
Washington Square Press, 1995, 180 pp., $10 (pb. reissue)

The reissue of Alexandra accompanies the motion-picture release of Mary Reilly, a film adaptation of Valerie Martin's best-selling novel. Alexandra is Martin's earlier book, set in Louisiana and focusing on the character of Claude Ledet.

Claude, who narrates the story, is

a middle-aged paper-shuffler living an uneventful life in New Orleans. Enter the mysterious Alexandra, and Claude's life begins to change. No sooner does he become involved with her than he finds himself doing things that amaze his best friend and co-worker, David, as well as himself. He uproots himself completely from his former life in order to follow his intoxicating lover to an estate deep in the Louisiana bayou. His association with Alexandra brings him into contact with two other women: Diana, the owner of the estate, and Collie, the servant who grew up with Alex and Diana. Both are as mysterious as Alexandra, and both seem to hold as many secrets—or are they all guarding the same one?

In this novel of gothic intrigue and sexual tension, billed as a "convergence of obsession, betrayal and murder," fine characterization is a surprising bonus. Even the minor characters are distinctive and well drawn, from Mona, the woman Claude leaves for Alexandra, to Banjo, a hermit who lives on the fringes of the bayou estate.

While the pace sometimes drags, the strange love story of Claude and Alexandra will keep the reader interested to the end. And despite the novel's billing, the resolution of the story rests as much on the dynamics of the characters as it does on the events which enfold them. Never does Martin fall back on cheap plot twists.

Intrigued readers of *Alexandra* will find themselves looking for more Valerie Martin titles not only at the bookstore, but at the cinema as well.

Of Love and Other Demons
by Gabriel García Márquez
Knopf, 1995, 147 pp., $21

Gabriel García Márquez's thirteenth book opens with a rabid dog loose in a Caribbean market, but the story begins much earlier. In his preface the author recounts his journalistic investigation, over forty-five years ago, of the burial crypt of a Clarissan convent. When workers broke open a vault, streams of copper hair spilled out until twenty-two meters of hair covered the floor. Tuning out the foreman's explanation that hair grows after death, García Márquez recalled an old legend of a girl with similar hair who was said to have performed miracles up and down the Caribbean coast.

Out of this mixture of myth and reality was born Sierva Maria de Todos los Angeles, the adolescent protagonist of his latest novel, who is propelled on a strange course of events after meeting the rabid dog in the market. The story is set in the eighteenth century, on a Caribbean island where Sierva's father, the Marquis, a descendent of Old World nobility, lives uneventfully with his mestiza wife Bernarda Cabrera. Married out of necessity, the Marquis delicately pines for his first wife, who was killed by a lightning bolt out of a clear sky, while Bernarda makes libidinous visits to the slave quarters and indulges an addiction to fermented honey. The neglected Sierva Maria is raised with the slaves, absorbing their hybrid religion of African deities and Catholic saints. After the dog in the market bites her, the magic she learned from the slaves is credited with protecting her from rabies. As ambiguous symptoms begin to appear, however, the Bishop declares that Sierva is possessed and decides to lock her away in part of a Clarissan convent once used as an Inquisition prison. Along the way, the reader learns why García Márquez places "love" in a category with "other demons."

While this short novel inevitably lacks the dazzling breadth of *One Hundred Years of Solitude*, once again García Márquez has produced a fresh and startling tale.

Pool

by Ajay Sahgal
Grove, 1995, 201 pp., $10 (paper)

Sahgal's first novel is the story of Emery Roberts, a young movie star who at the peak of his popularity decides to flee the set of his latest film and hole up at his brother's home in Vermont. Escape proves to be more difficult than he'd hoped, though, and most of the book chronicles Emery's inevitable fall back into movie life.

Sahgal, a veteran Hollywood screenwriter, brings an insider's knowledge to his story. Small details—the movie jargon, the cigarette after the gym—lend authenticity to the book, though not a single scene actually takes place in Tinseltown. Particularly noteworthy is Sahgal's gift for dialogue. The banter is constant, and while at times its utter *hipness* threatens to lose the reader, in the end, the characters' worldly discussions and one-liners are what bind the story together.

Relationships are begun and discarded almost as easily as the next drink is poured. Emery alone seems out of place—which is ironic since he is a Hollywood icon. His character, not quite intelligent enough to be jaded, displays instead a simple weariness with his surroundings. While his total acceptance of everything that happens sometimes seems implausible, ultimately it gives us insight into his mental

state, as well as providing us with an ideal perspective: the plastic hurricane of Hollywood life seen from the calm eye at its center.

The Fatigue Artist

by Lynne Sharon Schwartz
Scribner, 1995, 320 pp., $23

Lynne Sharon Schwartz has been publishing novels and short fiction for about fifteen years now, writing in a straightforward manner about the victories and defeats of modern urban life. Fans find her approachable, educational and witty. No minimalism from her, no ethereal, pseudo-plots and rarely any obscurity.

The protagonist of Schwartz's latest book is a forty-year-old novelist, Laura, suffering from Chronic Fatigue Syndrome. The novel follows her attempts to find a cure through Western medicine, Eastern medicine (including acupuncture and Tai Chi) and romance in the wake of her husband's murder. "I've got a virus that could go on awhile," Laura says of herself. "My immune system has surrendered. It's been insulted once too often. I'm a miniature ecological disaster, reflecting the larger global breakdown."

Set in New York, the novel employs illness as a metaphor. Even Laura's love affair with a mercurial actor, usually referred to as "Q," is compared to a virus, "impossible to dislodge." Schwartz can be funny and lyrical simultaneously, as in this passage about beds—a natural concern of someone who is always fatigued: "Why not go back to bed for awhile, I thought. I see the bed as my true home, my home within a home. Whoever invented it deserves as much renown as the inventor of the cotton gin or the steam engine, those inventions taught in school. People have always stretched out spontaneously on anything handy, yes, but I mean the combination of elements forming the bed itself. The raised platform, which makes climbing in a decisive event. The mattress and box spring, notions lovingly wrought. The feather pillow and the quilt are to repose what champagne and chocolate mousse are to diet."

The Fatigue Artist will surely resonate with all those busy souls who feel constantly tired and pressed for time.

Moo
by Jane Smiley
Knopf, 1995, 414 pp., $24

Comedy loves to lampoon bureaucracy and pretentiousness. Pulitzer Prize winner Jane Smiley's pleasure in the task is obvious in her latest novel *Moo*, a farcical indictment of academia. At her financially strapped midwestern university, nicknamed "Moo U," students are customers, professors are salespeople and administrators are CEOs driven mad by an ever-changing market. Smiley attacks every facet of campus life, and her depictions are always on-target. There are the gatekeeper secretaries who can make or break big deals by their handling of a single memo; there are the impressionable students, whose relationships mirror the corporate mentality of the university; and there are the self-absorbed professors, each convinced that not since the development of cloning has there been a research project as revolutionary as their own. Smiley's intricate plot moves outside the soon-to-be-condemned walls of the academy and infiltrates unexpected corners

of the world: the gold mines of Central America, the farms of the American Midwest, and even the tightly knit New York publishing world. Yet no matter where the story travels, the author's argument is always lurking under the paper trails of an out-of-control bureaucracy: higher education is driven by the lust for funds that only a well-written, profit-promising grant can obtain.

The Landlady in Bangkok
by Karen Swenson
Copper Canyon, 1994, 96 pp., $12

An undeniable political commentary murmurs beneath the surface of Karen Swenson's third volume of poems, set in Southeast Asia. The politics are acceptably liberal: disdain for early missionaries to the region; guilt over the Vietnam War; self-inculcating portraits of displaced orangutans and threatened lemurs. The result of such guilt-driven sympathies is that Swenson's less-than-original message occasionally mars the grace and lyricism of her verse. Fortunately, the carefully wrought imagery elevates the majority of the poems above the level of cliché. The closing image from a poem about exorcism, "The Balinese Witch Doctor," is as haunting as it is violent: "he [the witch doctor] scours for the demon ... while on the family altar the down on a headless baby chicken stirs."

In the course of her Southeast Asian journey, Swenson arrives at a wholly human perspective that considers the paradoxical human problems of loneliness versus the need for solitary adventure; guilt over war and ecological destruction versus the individual's inability to effect change. Swenson's brief sketches underscore what is universal in human nature.

Finally, though, it is the occasional and unique intrusion of Swenson's self into her Asian scenes that makes *The Landlady in Bangkok* a success rather than a mere curiosity as travel literature or as a political call against ecological and cultural destruction.

Montana 1948
by Larry Watson
Washington Square Press, 1995, 181 pp., $10 (pb. reissue)

Twelve-year-old David Hayden narrates this story of the rupture of a locally prominent family in eastern Montana just after World War II. David's father is the town sheriff, but since the sheriff's main jobs are chaperoning teenagers and drunken adults, he never carries a gun or a badge. His father's brother is a doctor, a war hero, and clearly the favorite son.

When David's Indian baby-sitter takes sick one day, his physician uncle mistreats her. From that point a mythic tale unravels, involving an elder son's hubris and a younger one's sense of duty. David's father gathers evidence for charges that are leveled against his brother and in the process discovers that the situation is much worse than he imagined. His own father, a rancher who represents the old laissez-faire ways of rural Montana, steps in on the side of his older son, and the whole town as well as the family splits over the scandal.

Watson tells his wonderful tale in a plainspoken, unromanticized style. The novel is marred only by an unnecessary coda. Half the pleasure in reading *Montana 1948* is in being transported to a place and time when there were fewer people,

when people remained loyal to their work and to the values that went with them.

Splitting
by Fay Weldon
Atlantic Monthly, 1995, 246 pp., $21

In her latest novel, *Splitting*, Weldon employs her trademark irony to turn the calamity of divorce into witty comedy. The title is an unabashed pun: The divorce of Angelica Rice and her husband, Sir Edwin Rice, causes not only a split between husband and wife, but also the hysterical splitting of Angelica into four distinct personalities. Her disintegration into Angel, a sexual dynamo, Jelly White, a hardworking secretary to her husband's attorney, and Lady Rice, a frail, romantic wimp, gets her into more trouble than even the worst of the town gossips could have imagined.

Angelica moves out of the Rice family home and begins to rally her separate personalities in order to fight the divorce. While the personality of Lady Rice wishes to stay in bed, sulk and pine for Edwin, Jelly White manages to organize Angelica's life and retaliate against her husband and his new mistress's attempts to strip her of her title. Meanwhile the libidinous Angel, despite the efforts of the other personalities to restrain her, takes over and creates even more trouble for Angelica by seducing Edwin's lawyer and a taxi driver—among other sexual escapades. Eventually Angelica's interests are protected; she sheds the false self who married Edwin (along with her other false "selves") and discovers the real Angelica.

Weldon's comic view of divorce and its effects on women is a refreshing change from the usual bleak treatment of the subject.

Worker-Writer in America: Jack Conroy and the Tradition of Midwestern Literary Radicalism, 1898-1990
by Douglas Wixson
University of Illinois, 1994, 678 pp., $34.95

The "worker-writers" of the 1920s and 1930s were a prolific but often overlooked group that contributed much to the history of modern literature. Now Douglas Wixson's *Worker-Writer in America* gives us a thorough treatment of this movement. Although in many ways a scholarly work—the notes and bibliography take up nearly 150 pages— this is also a riveting tale of the literary radicals. At the center is Jack Conroy, author of the novel *The Disinherited* and of many stories and essays. As a writer Conroy, born to a mining family in the Monkey Nest coal camp near Moberly, Missouri, stayed close to his working-class roots. He was the quintessential worker-writer: the son of an Irish immigrant miner and union leader who died in a mine accident, and an industrious mother who was widowed twice and raised seven children, three of whom died as young adults (two in mining accidents). Conroy himself entered the world of work at age thirteen, as an apprentice carman in the Wabash Railroad shop in Moberly. Following a railroad strike in 1922 he wandered the Midwest searching for employment, and during this time he began writing and meeting up with other working-class intellectuals. His sketch "Hard Winter" was accepted by H.L. Mencken's *American Mercury* in 1931, when Conroy was digging ditches and sleeping on a sandpile. *The Disinherited* was published in 1933. Conroy went on to edit two influential literary journals, *Rebel Poet* and *The Anvil;* the latter published early works by Richard Wright, Langston Hughes, Erskine Caldwell and Nelson Algren.

As a longtime friend of Conroy, and executor of his literary estate, Wixson had access to a mother lode of information, including letters between Conroy and other writers of the period. He also conducted numerous interviews with Conroy, who died in 1990. His portraits of Conroy and many others in the movement should spur new enthusiasm for these underappreciated worker-writers.

Easy Money
by Barbara Wright
Algonquin, 1995, 390 pp., $18.95

A successful life seems out of the question for Jay Winbourne, the central character of Barbara Wright's *Easy Money.* Her mother, dead since Jay was five, affords her no role model. Her father, Jack, is a crackpot and failure. And, the Ivy League colleges to which Jay aspires have all rejected her applications. So, leaving Denver and her father after high school graduation, she aims to make a life in New York, calling herself "Jacqueline" instead of Jay.

Easy Money is one of those staples of American literature, the coming-of-age story. But this one has a twist. Wright parallels the narrative of Jacqueline Winbourne's emergence into womanhood with the story of her father's maturing process in mid-life. Both of them begin to rise only when they realize the gifts they carry inside themselves. Her father's is a sensitivity for the speech patterns of his native region, which gives authenticity to his plays. It is Jacqueline's eye for colors and shapes that enables her to create striking sculptures out of castoff objects. Jacqueline creates her own patchwork life from bits and pieces: her family heritage, her random relationships, her native grit.

Face of a Stranger
by Yoji Yamaguchi
Harpercollins, 1995, $18

Japanese author Yamaguchi's debut novel is a revenge comedy about Japanese "picture brides," set in America in the early part of this century. The story begins with Takashi Arai, an irresponsible immigrant houseboy, whose only merit is his extremely handsome face. Unbeknownst to Takashi, his photograph is being used as that of a prospective husband to entice young Japanese brides-to-be to immigrate. At the end of the journey is no husband; instead the young women are forced into prostitution by the evil pimp, Kato.

The central character is Kikue, one of the deceived picture brides-turnedprostitutes, who sees Takashi one night and recognizes him as the handsome man whose photograph lured her. She and her friend Shino plan revenge, and hilarious chaos results.

Yamaguchi's cynical view of humanity is offset by his mastery of comic technique. This is a classic tale of mistaken identities, punctuated by slapstick and plenty of sharp, refreshing wit.

Reviews by:
Seth Bro, Anthony Butts, Andrew Careaga, Mary Creger, Virginia Fick, Jeff Galbraith, Reeves Hamilton, Kristen Harmon, Willoughby Johnson, Diedre Kindsfather, Speer Morgan, Hoa Ngo, Kirstin Rogers, Kylie Shafferkoetter, Kris Somerville, Jim Steck, Steve Weinberg, Roberta White, Melissa Wright

REMAINDERS & REMINDERS
Sam Stowers

Browsing the bargain bookstalls is something like combing a beach for shells. Often you don't recognize that there's a pattern to your finds until you get home, empty your pockets and arrange your treasures. When I sat down to write this column, I realized that I had picked up paperback copies of two first novels written by women who had solid reputations as poets before they turned to fiction. Both novels are autobiographical to some extent, and portray the coming of age of observant, vulnerable young people in turbulent times and difficult family circumstances. Engaging reads, they combine skilled recreations of crucial periods in history with vital portraits of individuals.

Diana O'Hehir's 1984 novel *I Wish this War Were Over* (Washington Square Press) takes place in the last year of World War II. The nation is on the move. The trains, train stations and hotels are packed. The fact that people of all ages, classes and regions are crammed into the same train compartments and hotel lobbies makes for improbable romance, a situation exploited by numerous wartime movies.

One of the many charms of this novel is that it exploits the dramatic possibilities of that interesting time with more complexity and energy than any of those old films did. A seemingly hapless nineteen-year-old woman, Helen, begins a cross-country train trip from Berkeley to Washington D.C. on a quixotic mission to save her alcoholic mother from herself. Along the way she encounters a married older man, an army lieutenant, who uses their coincidental proximity as an occasion to pester her for sex. The butt of her family's disorder, Helen is mothered by a younger sister and preached to by an imperious and uncaring grandmother. Looking to make a life of her own, she feels both threatened by and attracted to the lieutenant. O'Hehir's depiction of how she sorts out all her problems both overturns and at the same time answers the reader's expectations. It also provides the occasion for a string of high and low comic incidents. In Helen, O'Hehir has created an irresistible voice that brings to mind, at least fleetingly, a combination of Holden Caulfield's restless adolescent romanticism and Jane Austen's calm domestic realism.

I also picked up a British paperback edition of Jessica Hagedorn's 1991 *Dogeaters* (Pandora). This novel recounts the life of the city of Manila during thirty years of Philippine history, beginning in the 1950s and progressing through the rise and decline of Ferdinand Marcos. The story is told in a legion of voices, but those of Rio, an affluent Manila girl growing up in a corrupt home, and Joey, orphaned son of a prostitute, dominate the narrative and form a counterpoint coming-of-age story.

A montage of real and invented texts—poems, letters, soap operas and newspaper articles—augments Hagedorn's story. She quotes President McKinley and the Associated Press, and is as adept as Manuel Puig at describing movies as if we were seeing them projected. She mimics gangsters, politicians, academics, dressmakers and the delirious mental chatter of an Imelda-like first lady who dreams of George Hamilton, shopping in New York and sex with the Pope.

All this stylistic virtuosity serves an important narrative purpose: The Philippines is portrayed as a society of radical contradictions: peasants coexist with international capitalists, Catholics and Moslems with animists, and it is impossible to tell whether the city has invaded the jungle or vice versa. Philippine bloodlines blend European, Asian, and African races, and are the biological reflection of a history that cannot be told coherently. For Hagedorn, the incongruity of Philippine culture can only be compassed by a loose wrapping of popular culture composed of movies, beauty pageants, love songs, serial romances and pornography.

We are used to accounts of the cultural train wrecks that are the legacy of colonialism in the third world. But *Dogeaters* offers an absorbing variation on that theme for American readers. Beginning with the ceding of the Philippines to the United States after the Spanish American War, the histories of the two countries have been closely intertwined. Much of the popular culture that papers over the impossible contradictions in Philippine national life is derived from American sources. One of the collateral thoughts provoked by reading *Dogeaters* is the notion that in their separate ways, American society and Philippine society use the same trashy glitz to accomplish the same sort of desperate cultural camouflage.

SYCAMORE REVIEW

Fig. 7.1 Contemplating Life After Washington

INQUIRE
SUBSCRIBE
SUBMIT

POETRY FICTION ESSAYS VISUAL ART INTERVIEWS REVIEWS

Department of English Heavilon Hall Purdue University
West Lafayette Indiana 47907 Phone: 317/494-3783
E-mail comments & inquiries: sycamore@expert.cc.purdue.edu
WWW: http://expert.cc.purdue.edu/~sycamore/

Black Warrior Review

Karen Graffeo

Publishing the finest fiction, poetry, and essays
since 1974, and featuring the BWR chapbook series.

One of the "19 Magazines That Matter"

—*Writer's Digest*

"...the *Black Warrior Review* has become one of
our few indispensable literary magazines."

—*William Matthews*

Rita Dove
Gerald Stern
Greg Pape
Stephen Dobyns
Thomas Rabbitt
Christopher Buckley
Dara Wier
Mark Jarman
Chase Twichell
Marc Straus
Joy Williams
Rodney Jones
Richard Jackson
Andre Dubus
Tony Ardizzone
Beckian Fritz Goldberg
Mark Costello
Alison Baker
Sharon Sheehe Stark
Brendan Galvin
Alan Cheuse
Gary Soto
Jorie Graham
Marjorie Sandor
Albert Goldbarth
John Taggart
Beth Nugent

Sample copy $6, one year subscription $11
P.O. Box 2936   Tuscaloosa, Alabama 35486   205.348.4518

Distributed by Ingram Periodicals